To the Todts –

WARNING: This book contains cussing. ☺ I really am happy to know you all and hope you enjoy –

– Jeremy

# LOOK TO YOUR LEFT

# LOOK TO YOUR LEFT

JEREMY M. BURNSIDE

Cincinnati Book Publishing
Cincinnati, USA

# LOOK TO YOUR LEFT

A True Story of Law School Survival in the Face of Impossibility, Murder, and an Appalachian Apocalypse

By Jeremy M. Burnside



This is a work of creative nonfiction based upon a period in the author's life. The events, my participation in them, and my emotional reactions to them are true, to the best of my recollection. The dates, setting, and historical development of the school are correct. Using the literary techniques of the novelist, I have recreated or invented much of the dialog and some of the characters. I have changed some names, details, and altered dramatic situations to protect the anonymity of the people involved.

Cincinnati Book Publishing
Cincinnati, Ohio

Anthony W. Brunsman, President and CEO
Sue Ann Painter, Vice president and Executive editor
Cover design: Brent Beck
Editing and interior design: Mark P. Painter

Look to Your Left BOOK 978-0-9864238-0-2
Look to Your Left EBOOK 978-0-9864238-1-9
Library of Congress Control Number: 2015930688
Printed in the United States of America
First Edition, 2015

To purchase additional copies online, visit www.cincybooks.com
Discounts available on quantity orders. Email: info@cincybooks.com or call 513-382-4315.

www.cincybooks.com

# Foreword

Most lawyers look back on their law school days with a sense of horror and relief. As Jeremy Burnside reveals in this soul-searching book, law school is a testing ground that forces us to grow and ultimately, we hope, to become capable, caring lawyers.

I was fortunate to be able to pursue my law degree at the University of Cincinnati, where I had earned my undergraduate degree, made friends, and lived in a house near campus.

Jeremy Burnside's ordeal was much worse than mine was and much worse than most. Like many students, he struggled with grades and had squabbles with roommates and romantic interests. But he was far from home, friends, and family.

In what could only be called an Appalachian Apocalypse, the college town was afflicted with an explosion, which destroyed his apartment on the eve of final exams, and a flood. And three people, including the Dean, were murdered on campus. These horrendous incidents came on top of his failure to make grades in his first semester.

Jeremy was enrolled in America's newest and presumptively worst law school, the Appalachian State Law School, in rural Virginia, which was working toward accreditation. It had to have a worst student. Jeremy's grades were so low the first semester that he was placed on academic probation. But since he didn't totally flunk out (by a hair), he was still technically a law student. But his grade report said it all. *He was America's worst One L.*

With an amazing burst of determination, creative study techniques, and self-discipline, Jeremy learned to "think like a lawyer," and removed from almost certain expulsion. He became a first-rate law student, graduated, and passed the bar in Ohio and Kentucky. Burnside is now an outstanding trial lawyer in Portsmouth, Ohio.

As Jeremy tells us in this engaging story, he was faced with an almost impossible situation. Burnside's ability to go from academic probation to Dean's list in one semester was near miraculous. His experience, as related here, is a true story dramatized by fictional characters and conversations. It is a classic young man's coming-of-age tale set in an Appalachian "Paper Chase" environment. Jeremy's ordeal is alternately hilarious and perplexing, but ultimately heart-warming and inspiring.

In my thirty years as a trial and appellate judge, I observed thousands of people engaged in the practice of law. A few are brilliant and some are lacking—but most are sincere in their efforts to effect the best possible outcome for their clients. They struggle valiantly, drawing upon the resources they acquired in the stressful environment of law school.

The law is a demanding mistress, but she promises a meaningful life of service to those who survive the rigors of law school and studying for the bar. The young men and women who pursue careers in the law deserve our gratitude and respect. In a world of declining standards, the law remains one of the last true professions, and lawyers are guardians of our individual rights and liberties. Yes, some lawyers try to pervert the law and serve sinister interests. But they are the exceptions.

Lawyers like Jeremy Burnside exemplify the positive side of law—seeking justice for people, sometimes against long odds.

Mark P. Painter

*Judge, United Nations Appeals Tribunal 2009–2012*
*Judge, Ohio First District Court of Appeals 1995–2009*
*Judge, Hamilton County Municipal Court 1982–1995*

**Monday, March 25, 2002.**

**10:52 P.M.**

Tonight I care more about running out of beer than I do about my classmates saying I'm the next to go postal. After all, there are other ways for me to exact my revenge. I can just beat the overwhelming odds against me and pass.

There can be no bigger fuck-you than that.

# Preface

Becoming a lawyer is a bitch. As it should be. Our society charges lawyers to resolve wrong from right. From legislative bill drafting to court interpretations, lawyers shape the rules we live by. And it is because of this high sociological importance that law school has the right to strip you of three of your finest years, push you into a black hole of student loan debt, and then ultimately send you on a wild goose chase for a job.

Most prospective law students believe that the legal profession holds something special for them. Whether it is some sort of calling into public service, the prospect of big paydays, or a simple love of the law, thousands of people apply to the 200-ish law schools every year in the United States with the hope that their dreams will come true. Our American way of life fosters these dreams. But it is law school's job to destroy many of them.

It's not as if law school hides the fact that it is trying to fail you. It tells you at orientation, "Look to your left, now look to your right. One of you will not survive this first year." While it seems harsh that many law schools flunk a high percentage of students after the first year, it can be a blessing. Imagine having graduated, only to fail the bar exam and not become a lawyer. Worse, imagine having attended a full three years of law school, only to fail the final semester and not graduate. There is no refund policy on any of that tuition you paid and law school doesn't give a shit if your "dream" became a monthly student-loan-payment nightmare. But still, this is the way it needs to be. For you to overcome this perpetual risk is one way society gets the best out of you.

Though its methods are seemingly harsh, law school fosters something purely good: opportunity. If you are accepted into law school, you are presented with the great opportunity to prosper or the great opportunity to fail, depending how you look at things. If a law student knows how to study, remains confident, and above all else, is a strong person, they can make this opportunity into a wonderful experience. Law school classmates, despite the awkward competition that exists between them, develop friendships—the types you would see among war buddies. Despite the legend that most married law students become divorced, law students many times find their soulmates in law school. They pick up new talents and become better-disciplined people. Just like everything else in life, law school becomes what you make of it. And for some people, law school is a new lease on life.

To capture this opportunity and allow law school to academically haze you so that you can be a good lawyer in the new millennium, you have to first get in. One sad reality is that law school's prediction of your success, which is chiefly based on your LSAT score and undergraduate grades, is usually right. After all, law school needs something to gauge what type of student you will be and if you have what it takes to pass the bar exam. Your LSAT score shows law school the ability of your brain to analyze problems, while your grades represent your academic track record. It's usually a black-and-white determination, but sometimes, just sometimes, a law school will gamble on someone who falls short on either or both of these standards. I was one of those people and became very fortunate that one special law school gambled on me.

In 2001, I took my dream of becoming a trial lawyer to the Appalachian School of Law. I had an average G.P.A. of 2.9 and a LSAT score of 141, which was in the 13th percentile of all test takers. Today, those scores wouldn't get me accepted anywhere. But when I applied, the Appalachian School of Law was still new, and had to take its chances on slackers like me.

ASL opened in 1997 and was not fully accredited by the American Bar Association until several years after the events in this book took place. It is important that a law school be accredited, because it is necessary in most states for its law graduates to be able to sit for any given bar exam. While I attended, ASL was provisionally accredited. This meant that my class could sit for any bar, but did not guarantee the same for future classes.

The Appalachian School of Law is located in Grundy, Virginia—and at the time of my story, was surrounded by two gargantuan mountains, a Food City, and a Baptist church. Grundy is a small coal-mining town in Southwest Virginia, near the borders of West Virginia and Kentucky. It was founded in 1858 and named after Felix Grundy, former U.S. Attorney General, U.S. Congressman, and mentor of President James K. Polk. It's close to the childhood home of bluegrass legend, Dr.

Ralph Stanley, and was featured on the national stage in the 1980s when convicted murderer, Roger Keith Coleman, sparked a worldwide death-penalty debate.

Grundy didn't have a mall, bar, or identifiable city hall. I can remember Grundy having maybe three to four traffic lights spread out over the two main roads that made up a T that cut through the valley. For the things that Grundy lacked, it made up for with its overabundance of pharmacies, dollar stores, roadside flea markets and abandoned coalmines. Grundy may sound rough, but there was something about it that made me feel safe even in light of what you are about to read in this book.

Before you begin reading my personal One L story, there are several things you should know. First, you must know up front that many of the characters in my story are fictional. They don't intentionally (or subliminally) resemble one person in particular. Rather, I based each fictional character on real feelings I received from several different people along my journey. This is a dramatized coming-of-age story and is not intended to be an accurate play-by-play historical recount of who-said-what. For this literary sacrifice, I am able to give you a no-holds-barred look into my soul.

Second, you will read about several different tragedies that occurred in Grundy during the spring semester of 2002. Though these events may sound far-fetched, they happened. All of them. The places I go and the things that I do are also real. But the most important truth you will read about, and the focus of my story, is what I was feeling during this defining time of my life.

My story would not be genuine if I did not exhibit the harshness I felt towards the Appalachian School of Law and the people of Grundy during my One L journey. But before my story begins, I don't want there to be anything left to doubt: I love Grundy, Virginia, including its people, places, and perseverance. With its recent growth, Grundy is attacking undeserving stereotypes and becoming an even more wonderful place to live. I am proud to have attended the Appalachian School of Law, which continues to fulfill its mission by providing better legal counsel to struggling areas of rural Appalachia. I am honored that Grundy and ASL welcomed me and gave me an opportunity to personally evolve.

If my first year of law school had occurred in any other place or at any other school, I would have succumbed to the distractions that come with more civilization and would have surrendered to what others deemed impossible.

# Chapter 1

Life-defining moments begin when sanity is threatening to end. It was January 11, 2002, and I was awaiting results of my epically reckless first year fall semester of law school. I was a One L at the Appalachian School of Law in Grundy, Virginia. Well, at least I thought I was.

Vomit was stirring in the pit of my stomach and I could taste its release in the base of my throat. My anxiousness that day came from my belief that ASL was giving my classmates and me one more dose of torture before releasing our fall semester grade reports.

We all had a rough fall semester—adjusting to Grundy, one another, and the competitive circumstance of our One L existence. That's not to mention 9/11, which tragic events occurred soon after we all met. We had classmates who suffered losses that day, which I believe forged some type of special bond between us and gave me another excuse to drown my sorrows that semester. While some of us took a few steps back after 9/11, others got inspired and seemed to study harder "for America." These academic patriots were ASL's One L elite, or what I called the All-Stars.

We were all paralyzed with fear on that uncharacteristically sunny January day. Even the All-Stars. They enrolled at ASL for customary graduate reasons like wanting to stay close to home, or for getting a big scholarship. But even the All-Stars were sweating it out like the rest of us desperate misfits, who were at ASL for the obvious reason that few other, and no better, schools had accepted us, and we just wanted to live to see another One L day. The All-Stars had higher aspirations. They worried about their Law Review chances, "booking" a class (achieving the top score), or at worst, making the coveted Dean's List. I envied the shit out of those people, and for at least those few weeks in January, I wanted to be sitting in their seats, to the left of me.

For those of us who were terrible-to-average undergraduate students, or bad test-takers, or both, it wasn't just the financial risk we took by taking the law-school plunge that made us worry so much. My fellow misfit comrades gave up good jobs they worked hard for, ended things with their spouses, or left their families behind in their home states. For me, I sacrificed my good state job, broke up with my college sweetheart, and made my friends and family believe that I would be somebody. We all took life-changing risks. And we certainly all had our own reasons for needing to walk out those classroom doors still alive as law students.

We were sitting in Criminal Law class that day. Many of my classmates were on their laptop computers, instant messaging one another about the latest gossip. My girlfriend of three months, and leader of the All-Stars, Lois Stanley, was working on her study group's meeting schedule. Some of the lectern trolls in the front row made it look like they were typing notes, but they were all emailing who-knows-who. We all had a feeling that ASL would distribute our grades before the weekend, to allow the dust to clear before the survivors would return on Monday.

In a reckless attempt to calm my nerves, I read online articles about the "The Drive." That day was the fifteenth anniversary of when the Denver Broncos knocked my beloved Cleveland Browns out of Super Bowl contention after the most famous offensive drive in football history. Reading the commemorative stories about how the Browns defense played not-to-lose rather than to win was actually making me more anxious for my grades. Like the Browns defense, I was afraid to fail and applied no aggression to the way I studied. And just like how, as an eight-year-old boy, I felt helpless watching John Elway march down the field towards a Denver victory, there was nothing I could do to stop what I was sure to be my imminent loss to the law school establishment.

Sitting expressionlessly in the back was Nigerian-naturalized citizen and repeat One L, Peter Odion-Iyore Odighizuwa. Peter O, as we called him, was one of the few minorities believed to be partly responsible for ASL's recent ABA provisional accreditation, an important piece of ASL's ultimate plan. Because of Peter O's presumed significance to ASL's existence, Dean L. Anthony Sutin, the man who delivered our "look to your left" speech, had provided him several chances to get his grades up. But because of a string of missed classes and failure to turn in the most important assignments, everyone believed that Peter O was surviving on borrowed time. Everyone, that is, except for Peter O.

The clock struck noon as the double doors of ASL's appellate courtroom finally swung open. My class collectively gasped.

Dean Paul Lund, Assistant Dean of Students and a noticeably hard thinker who walked with what one could consider a rapper's strut, was the first through the doors. He was eyeing the floor, noticeably avoiding eye contact with anyone. The news was so bad that he brought a posse to help him convey it—Vickie Keene, admissions director, Regina Sweeny, admissions secretary, and Nancy Pruitt, admissions counselor, trailed Dean Lund. The admissions staff members were the first faces we saw when we all toured. For many of us, they would be the last faces we'd see at ASL.

Dean Lund stood in front of the lectern and cut straight to the ugly.

"I'm sorry to announce that five of you are no longer One Ls. Five of you received a GPA of a 1.67, or lower, and will not return on Monday."

I turned around and looked up at Peter O. Surely, his time had run out. I was certain he was one of the five. Then the local guy, Blugg, he had to be number two.

Maybe I'm three. Or five.

Dean Lund continued, "ASL is also placing another handful of you on academic probation. If you don't know, academic probation is an academic classification for anyone receiving a GPA under the requisite 2.0, but over 1.67."

Vickie was a very nice lady who always made good eye contact. Not then; her eyes were focused to an unknown place along the east wall. Regina always had a big smile on her face. She was not smiling that day. Nancy appeared to be trembling. It seemed they were all worried that someone wouldn't take the news of failure so well.

I looked to my left and looked to my right. The people around me seemed too smart.

I got drunk for a final.

I skipped a lot of classes.

I didn't take my studies seriously.

I deserved to fail.

Upon locating his master list, Dean Lund started calling out our assigned student numbers. Dean Lund's timid voice was amplified in our minds, aided by the dead silence of the room.

One by one, my fellow classmates approached the front center lectern to receive their fall semester fortunes. Their feet hit the hardwood floors like rhythmic drum beats: step, step, step, step. The distributor, Vickie Keene, did her best to offer a comforting glance to each of my classmates as she handed them their envelopes.

I felt like I was going to pass out.

Of the people I knew well, I noticed Charlie Vincent go first. If the New Jersey Guido suffering from little-man syndrome failed out, I would feel partly responsible. After all, I had constantly pressured him to get drunk, didn't help him in our study group, and was a bad friend when his cousins were killed on 9/11. Charlie shuffled to his right, contemplated opening his envelope right there, but shook his head and quickly retreated out of the room.

Lois was next. Although I appreciated her taking me in to her All-Star study group when Charlie kicked me out of his group, I partially blamed her for how much of a nut job I was during the fall semester. While Lois was a decent companion, she was a horrible classmate. When we were together, she always pressured me about studying. She'd say things like, "Oh no, Jeremy. You don't have so-and-so outline done? Aren't you worried about that? You should be." When she received her grade report, she confidently slipped it in her purse and walked out the door.

Grundy's native son, Bluggton Wayne Carr, approached moments later, his heavy footsteps on the hardwood sounding like a bass drum. On the first day of orientation, I overheard some of my classmates seriously debate whether he could fully read and write. Blugg, as everyone called him, was a clear victim of darn-right meanness, but did some things you couldn't help but to laugh at. Once Vickie handed Blugg his envelope, he fumbled it on the floor. As he bent over to pick it up, his butt crack flashed those of us who were remaining.

My law school nemesis, Todd Criscuola, the Dickhead from Darlington, South Carolina, was next. He had been intent on my failure and had targeted Lois's vagina during the fall semester. As he snatched his envelope from Vickie, he zapped a fuck-you look my way. His broad shoulders, arrogant strut, and goofy grin made it look like he had just accepted the Heisman. He sat down in the front row of seats and opened his grade report for everyone to see his reaction. Upon glancing at the document, he lifted his fist in the air and blurted out what sounded like, "Suck it!"

Then my roommate Tater Thayer accepted his envelope, bouncing and smiling like he was receiving a kindergarten diploma. The former high school basketball star opened his envelope, glanced at the document inside, and then brought it lovingly to his lips where he kissed it. As he made his way towards the doors, Tater shot a fake jump shot at the doorframe.

Portia Simmons, ASL's queen of competitiveness, opened her envelope before she would allow the next One L to advance. She then jubilantly turned and faced the few of us who remained and yelled, "Yes! 3.4!" I thought I saw her blow a read-it-and-weep kiss my way, but my mind wasn't clear enough for me to be sure.

Looking around the room, I noticed that just two of us remained. Peter O was still sitting calmly in the back. Observing. Seemingly calculating.

Then Dean Lund's voice echoed--and echoed—when he announced, "At last, 0077980, please come forward."

I debated whether I should've just left to get it later. My march to the front of the room wasn't at all a rhythmic drumbeat. I slowed and stopped and accelerated and stopped. I felt like I was going to collapse from dizziness as I stumbled closer to Vickie. The room was spinning and I was sweating profusely. She handed me the last envelope and then immediately turned away to join the others who already made a quick escape into the outside hallway. No calming glance for me.

It felt like Vickie Keene had just handed me a death telegram. Once I clutched my envelope, I almost took a nosedive. After steadying myself, Peter O, in his broken English and noticeably without his own grade report, called down from the back of the room, "Jed-a-me," he said, "I will never forget what you did."

I waved and got the hell out of there. At that moment, Peter O's problem with me was nothing compared to what I held in my hands. I opened the appellate courtroom doors and bolted to the most immediate private place I could think of, a men's restroom stall, where I sat down. I pulled on the single piece of paper, stopped and took a deep breath. I took another deep breath. And a few more. Brain in a tizzy.

I hope I didn't abandon the good life I created for myself in West Virginia for nothing.

I can't go back to my hometown in Ohio a failure.

I just can't . . .

I opened the envelope and tried not to view the final GPA until I had looked at all of the grades on the paper. Right off the bat, I knew I was doomed. My grade report read, Contracts I—D, followed by, Property I—C+, which gave me hope, then, Torts—D+, and again, Civil Procedure I—D+. As my heart was dropping and the world was collapsing around me, I read, Legal Process I—B-.

I thought the C+ and B- were possibly enough. I then contemplated lifting my shaky, sweaty, right digits off my GPA. I wasn't ready. Staying conscious was difficult. My heart was beating out of my chest as Todd Criscuola, walked in, talking to one of his cronies. I heard him say, "Peter O finally failed out. He's already going around trying to get people to help him."

Once the restroom cleared, and after one last deep breath, I moved my hand and began to open my eyes. I squinted to take in a sliver of light, which provided a sliver of sight. My grade report read, Semester GPA—1.73.

Shit.

Oh, shit.

America's newest and presumptively worst law school had to have a worst student. Since I didn't totally fail out, I was still technically a law student. But my grade report said it all.

With Peter O gone, I was America's worst One L.

# Chapter 2

After I barfed, my suspected coronary subsided. With my head pounding and my legs like Jell-O, I retreated out a back door and found what I hoped to be safe haven on a hidden curb behind a dumpster. Any sense of ambition I once had to become a lawyer came to an abrupt halt.

In that telling piece of paper, the law school establishment spelled out the legitimacy of my law school enrollment decision and direction of my future. As a 23-year-old fantasist, my dream of becoming a lawyer had turned into a nightmare. I was certain that blind optimism had led me to the biggest, most expensive mistake of my life.

I sat motionless. Then out of nowhere, the back door flew open and I heard the voice of the last person I wanted to talk to at that moment. Like a coondog that caught the scent of a wounded squirrel, Lois found me.

"Hey, you'll never guess what I got!"

She must have seen me leave. I quickly hid my grades in my armpit and looked up. Lois stole a kiss on my cheek and plopped down on my lap.

"Guess my GPA!"

I covered my mouth and looked the other way as I addressed her.

"Well, Lois," I said in a soft monotone, "whatever it was, I guarantee it's better than what I got."

"Please tell me that you're not one of the five."

"No, but..."

Oblivious to my dejection, Lois shoved her grade report in front of my face. It read, Semester GPA 3.6. She stood up, shimmied her ass with glee, and said, "I beat Portia and should be number one!"

Lois was too ecstatic to comfort me so I got up and started walking away.

"Hey, aren't you happy for me?" she asked.

"I've got to get back. Talk to you later."

I walked outside ASL for a few minutes staring at the dead leaves scattered around. Lois didn't follow; she knew better. After all, I had been a downer much of the short time we dated and she had learned to stay away when I became worried.

After about twenty minutes of wishing I could do it all over, I finally gathered the courage to walk to the Johnson Building, which served as my apartment building and the sitting Buchanan County judge's old law office. The Johnson Building was great for studying because it had its own law library overlooking the Grundy Flood Control Project, the official name for the Army Corps of Engineers' process of "moving the town" across the Levisa River. In April 1977, the water got 22 feet above flood stage resulting from sixteen inches of rain in three days. With most of the coal mines closed, another flood like the one Grundy experienced in 1977 would surely kill the town.

I liked the Johnson Building because of the kick-ass parties I had hosted during the fall semester, but I'd been in its law library only once—before I started dating Lois, after a party, when a local girl volunteered to show me her boobs.

When I got to the Johnson Building, I made a beeline to my bedroom, ignoring Tater's request to see my grade report. I felt depressed, angry, and disenchanted. But I had it coming. Even after I got kicked out of my fall semester study groups, I nevertheless attempted to secure the completed group outlines—cowardly acts of sheer desperation. I was an academic freeloader. I asked for a lot, but gave nothing.

Unable to think about anything other than being a near-certain failure, I began throwing things across the room. In a display of temper I had only shown after Art Modell moved my Cleveland Browns to Baltimore, I reached to rip my law school denial letters off the wall. Then I stopped, dropped to the floor, and looked up at the collage of rejection I had originally hung to motivate me.

Pepperdine. Catholic. American.

They were all right about me.

Soon the rage wore off and I sensibly began thinking of my alternatives. I needed to know just how severe my probation was and if I'd be prolonging the inevitable to the tune of thousands more in loans if I stayed. At my desk, I calculated what GPA it would take to get me into good standing. It was worse than I had thought. During that spring semester, I was going to need to score in the top 10% in the class. That meant at least all Bs, sprinkled with at least one B+ and an A. With ASL's unforgiving bell curve designed to give students lower grades so they couldn't transfer, I didn't think I stood a chance. At that moment, I felt that the LSAT was right about me.

In one of my rejection letters, the University of the Pacific stated, "For a number of applicants (aka, me), Law School Admissions Test results were not competitive..." Just like my ACT results for undergraduate admission, I received the lowest score any institution would take. My LSAT score, a 141, landed me in the thirteenth percentile of all test takers. As a result, ASL was one of only two schools, out of the twenty-six I applied to, to accept me. As I sat there contemplating my next move, I wished I had trusted the LSAT's ability to statistically predict law school failure.

Once I collected myself, I frantically walked back over to ASL to see if my academic advisor, Professor Tom Blackwell, had any guidance. Professor Blackwell was a jolly-looking Texan who was stern, but fair. He was the type of guy I could explain my seemingly hopeless situation to and still hope to receive some type encouragement—even if it was after a Texas tongue-lashing.

When I got to Professor Blackwell's office, the door was unfortunately shut. Desperate for advice, any advice, I went from the closed door of my most compassionate professor and trusted advisor, to the open door of a scoundrel.

I walked into the office of Civil Procedure Professor Richard E. Eisen and said, "Professor, I was wondering if you had a minute."

I had no respect for the man. I called him Dickey, but not to his face. He was six foot-four-ish and built like a brick shithouse. The fake-tanned, well-dressed asshole was sitting in his chair with his back facing the door and me when I walked in. Without turning to see who was beckoning him, Dickey said, "A minute for what?"

"I'm feeling pretty lost right now. My fall semester GPA was a..."

With his back still towards me, Dickey interrupted, "If this has anything to do with your grade, you'll have to take it up with Paul Lund. My grading system is fair."

"This isn't about my grade. I want your counsel about something."

I closed the door before Dickey could object. I said, "Professor, I've been placed on academic probation. In fact, I'm now .06 from completely failing out. That's a 1.73 GPA. What do I do?"

Dickey was not interested in engaging. His back remained towards me and it looked like he was reading a newspaper. Dickey only mustered up a quick breath to say, "I cannot comment."

"But Professor…"

Dickey then swiveled his chair around to face me. He was angry that someone was wasting his time and he seemed even angrier that it was me seeking his precious counsel. In just one semester, out of the dozens and dozens of students he taught in all of his classes combined, Dickey developed a strong dislike for me. His "I can't believe you came to my prestigious class looking like that" demeanor suggested that it had something to do with my heavy metal tee shirts and wild hair.

"Well, Mister Burnside, in my experience, the fall semester is very indicative of how you will do throughout the rest of your law school career. What did you get on your LSAT?"

I paused.

Just give it to him.

"It wasn't the greatest score. I got under a 150."

Dickey smirked. "Under 150? How did you possibly get accepted to any institution? Frankly, if you got less than a 152 on the LSAT, you probably had no business even applying for law school. If you want my advice, go home, find another career and think of the past five months as an expensive learning experience. Meanwhile, I need to have a talk with our admissions people for letting those scores into my classes."

Standing there, no doubt with a stupid look on my face, I didn't know what to do. I was shocked, but, then again, I knew I had invited Dickey's insults. He had only told me what I needed to hear. Without further comment, I left his office. On any other day, I would have told him to fuck off and kiss my ass. On that day, however, I thought that maybe Dickey was right.

⚖

Before following Dickey's instruction and packing up to go home to Cleveland, I walked around to the other side of the building and down the stairs that led to the admissions office. I wanted to say good-bye to Vickie, Regina, and Nancy. When I toured ASL, their personalities made Grundy seem like a happy place. I truly believed that Vickie took a gamble on me after reading my personal statement in my admissions application. My undergraduate GPA of 2.9 definitely didn't offset my LSAT score. My over-the-top statement highlighting how I grew up on and off government assistance had to be why I got in.

As I approached the stairwell, I heard some heated conversation. A loud male voice in broken English echoed from the direction of the office of my Legal Process professor, Mrs. Idame Jean Frehley. Although I couldn't make out what he was saying, it was apparent that Peter O was much more desperate than I was.

Maybe he had finally cracked.

Mrs. Frehley was a former prosecutor from New York City, accent still intact. Her beloved husband had died a few years earlier so she had decided to take a lower-tiered professorship at ASL to be close to her son, a supervisor for the flood-control project. Mrs. Frehley was about sixty-five years old, the oldest professor at ASL. Although by far our most engaging professor, the rumor was that she was so distressed that ASL hired her at such a low pay grade that she declined the "Professor" title.

I tried to approach Mrs. Frehley's office silently, but my Chuck Taylor's squeaked on a section of the floor, echoing down the hall. The noise must have startled Peter O; he abruptly left Mrs. Frehley's office grasping some papers. As he walked hurriedly past me, we made eye contact for a split second. The redness of his eyes matched the anger bleeding through his face. He was mad, but then again, he always was. Peter O said to me, "You watch out."

Under my breath, I replied, "You go fuck yourself."

I peeked my head into Mrs. Frehley's office. She was taking deep breaths. I said, "Are you okay?"

Mrs. Frehley put on a fake grin and said, "Oh, yes, thank you. Just fine. Is there something I can help you with, Jeremy?"

"No, I don't think so. I heard Peter O from down the hall. I also had a run in with him last semester, a few actually. I think he and I now have a lot in com . . ."

I hesitated. I wanted to tell her how Peter O and I were similar in academic stature. I wanted someone to comfort me. I was still desperate and just needed a caring ear. I couldn't resist talking about it.

"Mrs. Frehley, since I'm here, I was hoping you could help me with something. ASL placed me on academic probation and I'm in too much of a hole to dig out. I've decided to call it a day and return home to the big city."

"Oh?"

"I don't know why Peter O was here —my guess is that you failed him. I guess I can see why he might be freaking out because I am, too."

Mrs. Frehley looked confused. She leaned back in her wooden desk chair.

"But you're only on probation. Why are you giving up so easily?"

"Because I would need a miracle to bring my grades to a 2.0. I would have to make Dean's List this semester, at the minimum."

Mrs. Frehley began rocking in the chair. My concerns somehow relaxed her—she seemed to be breathing easy again after her showdown with Peter O. She said, "What did you receive in my class?"

"B minus."

"Oh yes! I remember the B minus grade because it was the only one I gave out. You did a great job in my class, although your use of quotes needs considerable work."

"But I'm terrible at timed exams. Always have been. Almost didn't graduate high school because of the state math-proficiency test. Your class, no offense, was easy for me because I wasn't under a clock."

"Jeremy, it sounds like you have a pretty impossible task ahead of you. Quitting makes the most sense right now, but I'd hate to see you give up. In my opinion, Legal Process is the most important law school class. It helps students see what the practice of law is all about."

Mrs. Frehley sat up when she concluded, "Jeremy, if you can't perform under the clock, you probably won't pass any bar exam, but you can use a law school degree for many other careers."

Well, that just about makes it official.

I have no chance.

I thanked Mrs. Frehley for her time and left. When I got back to the Johnson Building, I found my Two L mentor, who was also my other roommate, Dennis Mensinger, walking around my bedroom—investigating. I had been avoiding him since grades came out. I felt like I had let him down. Dennis gave me a lot of advice and I ignored every word of it. Ashamed, I approached him and said, "Hey man. What a mess. I'm leaving."

In a comforting tone, Dennis said, "You were one of the One L five?"

"Yeah, pretty much."

"What do you mean, pretty much?"

"I'm on academic probation."

Dennis lit up a cigarette and said, "So? At least you have another chance."

"Well, maybe, but Mrs. Frehley said it would probably be impossible and Professor Eisen, well, he wonders how I even got into law school to begin with."

"Eisen's an asshole. I wouldn't put any stock in what he said. What did you end up getting? A 1.91 isn't too bad. You didn't get a 1.85 or something, did you?"

I replied with embarrassment, "No, 1.73."

Dennis choked on his cigarette smoke and began to cough.

While not quite regaining clear breath, he said, "Oh fuck. Maybe you might have been better off if you failed out. That's a terrible spot, really. Horrible."

Looking for elder student perspective to what I believed was the obvious decision, I said, "Den, be honest, if you were in my shoes, you would leave, right?"

Dennis took a few moments to respond and finish clearing his throat.

"Hell yeah. No one can come back from that. Especially not you after the recklessness you displayed last semester."

Maybe I didn't want him to be that honest.

"Do you mean to tell me that there's no chance I can come back from a 1.73 GPA to become a Two L?"

"That's exactly what I'm saying. It's impossible."

# Chapter 3

I took my lumps growing up in the dying near west side of Cleveland, Ohio. Appalachian Americans who lost work in the coalmines and came to Cleveland to work in steel factories were the cornerstones of my old neighborhood. Some folks called this journey from the mountains to the former fountains of industry the "Hillbilly Highway." My paternal grandfather, a WWII veteran and an unemployed coal miner from Clay County, West Virginia, called it necessity. Nevertheless, when most of these good folks got older or lost their steel jobs in Cleveland, they went back to the hills in what became known as the Reverse Appalachian Migration. That's when the guns and the gangs took over the neighborhood.

As I left Grundy, I decided that I would live with my dad, "Hammer" Mike Burnside, in his rundown cottage on West 48th Street, or what the locals referred to as "Marijuana Alley." Hammer Mike was his bar name. He got it because he'd often approach any broken item needing repair by saying, "Some cold beer and a hammer oughtta fix that!"

I got in late that night, but early enough that the drug dealers and gang bangers weren't prowling just yet. I went to the back door and fumbled with my keys, trying to find the right one. Suddenly, the door swung open and Hammer Mike answered by pointing his revolver right at my face. It was his security feature to match the neighborhood's charm. I didn't tell him I was coming, but luckily Hammer Mike recognized his spitting image through the sights of his .45 Smith & Wesson.

"What the fuck, son? I could've shot your ass!" He put the pistol down.

"Sorry dude, I should've called."

Waiving me into the house, he said, "Fuckin' A, right you should've called. Maybe once you become a lawyer you can afford a fuckin' cell phone."

My dad was a fixture of the old neighborhood, a perfect representation of what was and who had left. He was a city steel hauler by trade, but just a good ole West Virginia boy at heart.

Hammer Mike said, "So what the fuck are you doing here? Aren't you supposed to be in school?"

"Dad, we're going to need some beer for this."

Hammer Mike and I made a deal almost two years prior. I'd go to law school and he'd go to trucking school. He passed within no time and it was my turn to live up to my end of the bargain. I dreaded telling him the news that I had quit. My dad shoved his arms through his worn leather coat, snugged his Harley Davidson hat over a pronounced mullet, popped in a Marlboro Red, and waved me out the door.

"Then we're going to Henry's. You're driving, I'm drinkin'."

My dad was proud of being a truck driver. After years without steady employment, hauling steel in his Mack truck named Penelope was his pride and joy. He wasn't going to get another DUI and I believed him, for the most part.

Henry's Bar, just a few blocks over, was locally famed for its permanent drunks, sporadic murders, and nightly bar brawls. As I drove, I noticed several more houses boarded up and littered with the customary graffiti.

Hammer Mike spent all of his free time at Henry's. With a hodgepodge of West Virginia University and Confederate flags covering the walls and moonshine available upon request, Henry's was a reminder of what the neighborhood used to be—blue-collar redneck. Despite their appetite for trouble, its patrons all loved and respected my dad. He was one of them. They all treated me like a son and I, in turn, considered them family.

Just as many of my classmates had fathers who were lawyers, doctors, or other sorts of scholars, so too, did I. Hammer Mike was a professor of Henry's School of Hard Knocks. The folks at Henry's often listened to his curricula of bad fortune and how he overcame it—or whose ass he kicked if he didn't. In addition to his teaching duties, Hammer Mike also worked in Henry's kitchen, handing out knuckle sandwiches anytime anyone "asked for it."

My dad always claimed he was proud of having a son striving to fight on the opposite side of the law. And for that, I wasn't just a family member, I was Henry's royalty. When I walked into Henry's late that night, I sat in my reserved bar stool and a beer magically appeared in front of me, as they always seemed to do. I felt like the owner, Henry, always kept that bar stool open for me, just in case I were to blow in.

After three beers, two bags of pork rinds, and one long story about how local roofer Ponytail John was getting screwed over by his "old lady," I had built up enough fortitude to break the news to Hammer Mike. I took a big swig of beer and said, "Dad, I failed law school."

"Get the fuck out of here." Hammer Mike chugged the rest of his beer and pretended I didn't say anything.

"Seriously, dude, I failed out. I didn't follow instructions on my Torts final, was drunk for my Contracts final, and couldn't concentrate after my professor pissed me off right before my Civil Procedure exam. Then I shit my pants over thinking I turned in someone else's memo in Legal Process. I fucking blew it."

Hammer Mike slammed his hat to the floor and shook his head in disappointment.

"You were drunk for a test? What the fuck is wrong with you, boy?"

"Dude, I mentally lost it. I wasn't ready for law school. I never studied in college and it came back to bite me."

"Son, ain't nobody from this family ever got as far as you. I'm having a hard fucking time believing this shit."

After ordering another Bud Light, I said, "Well, I actually didn't officially fail out. They placed me on probation. A very deep academic probation."

"Probation? Shit, son, I've been on probation. Granted, it was after doing time at the work house, but it's temporary."

Hammer Mike always had a simple solution to everything. As he stopped me from opening my new beer, he swiveled his stool towards me and said, "You're not fucking quitting. Instead, your ass is getting up with me and I'm going to show you just what the fuck you'll be doing if you stay here."

"But, dad. I can't pass. It's impossible."

"Damn it, boy, if it was impossible, probation wouldn't exist, now, would it?"

"When you wallow with the pigs, expect yourself to get dirty," Hammer Mike said with a smile, as I stepped into a large mud puddle covered by a thin sheet of ice just five hours after we stumbled out of Henry's. In the lake-effect cold, I spent the day with Hammer Mike and Penelope strapping down smashed metal vehicles to the flatbed trailer. I couldn't feel my fingers or toes and Penelope's heater didn't quite work to warm them. I had previously worked on a garbage truck and felt I could handle the blue-collar Cleveland lifestyle. It would toughen me up. But as frostbite was likely setting in, I already began to have significant doubts about working in my dad's shoes.

Hammer Mike often described himself as a horse trader. From one junkyard to the other, my dad was always working some angle on a beat-up car or a part for his 1974 Harley Davidson Shovelhead. If I ever needed something, my dad found a way to barter for it. For example, before I left for college, my car, which my dad traded two dirt bikes for, was in bad shape. He traded a shitload of moonshine in exchange for a Bondo and paint job. I could tell that it bothered him that he couldn't trade something for me to have good grades.

Hammer Mike gave up on the Browns after The Drive, but never gave up on me. Growing up, he'd often leave our family for West Virginia on extended "drunks," but he always eventually came back. During our steel haulin', and when I was "cryin' the blues," as he called it, Hammer Mike asked me why I just didn't leave that semester, go back to West Virginia, study-up and re-enroll the next year—ready to achieve what others hailed as impossible. West Virginia was safe haven for us Burnsides, but I knew I'd have a hard time facing the important people in Charleston who encouraged me to go to law school to begin with.

The wind was kicking up, and I was miserable. In the back of my mind, my life in Grundy would have seemed like a vacation, even from that one day of work. Towards the end of the long day, I looked towards the immediate future.

"Hey dad, when do we have to go out tomorrow?"

With a smirk, Hammer Mike said, "Shit, son, if they call us at eleven tonight, we go at eleven tonight."

Fuck.

Sensing my misery, Hammer Mike said, "So, bub, you like being a steel hauler?"

With absolutely no truth in my response, I said, "Yeah, sure. Not bad at all. Beats hanging around asshole law professors or taking orders from senators, like what I did in Charleston."

"You sure about that?"

I didn't want my dad to think I was a wimp, so I responded, "Burnside Trucking. It has a nice ring to it."

Hammer Mike lit a cigarette and said, "It sure does. But bub, if I was you, I'd rather jump barefoot off a six-foot step ladder into a five-gallon bucket full of porcupines than be doing this shit with my dad."

"Seriously dad, I can do this."

My dad would often say that he was born at night, "but not last night." He knew I was miserable and that he got his point across. Hammer Mike parked Penelope in her resting place and shook his head.

"Well, son, I hate to do this to you, but you aren't welcome at my house, or in my town for that matter."

"Huh?"

"We both know damn well that if you stay here, you'll be a big ole sack of shit. You'll always think about that time you quit law school. My advice, son, is to try—and if you fail, well, shit, at least you weren't no quitter. And although I love you, I won't hang out with your mopey-quitter-ass attitude day in and day out. I thought I raised you better than that."

"Come on dude, for real? That's your solution? You're kicking me out of Cleveland? That's ridiculous."

"Son, go back to West Virginia and remind yourself of why we made our little deal to go to school in the first place."

# Chapter 4

"And Senator, while I'm fetching that coffee, you can go fuck yourself," were the last words I spoke before sending out my first law school application. It was February 2001 during the West Virginia legislative session and I had had enough of being Senator Wiley P. Kulick's bitch.

Senator Kulick was about 75 years old and had a creepy permanent smile that I imagined came from a turnip being shoved far up his ass. He may have been in the legislature a long time, but I didn't care enough about him to check. All that was relevant to me was that the senate president recently appointed him to my committee and I had to do what Kulick said. I was the proud legislative analyst for Chairman William R. Wooton and worked with some of the most dedicated people I had ever met. Since Senator Kulick joined Chairman Wooten's judiciary committee, however, I started to feel less like a part of the team and more like a glorified copy boy."

After a lax Friday committee meeting, Senator Kulick finally noticed that I was placing the wrong bills in his binders. Although he acted as if he was reading the bills during the meetings, he never did. Senator Kulick was a lawyer on the most important legislative committee in the senate in my paternal ancestor state; I was offended that he wasn't genuinely embracing his charge. So since the previous week, I set him up to verify to myself that he was, indeed, ignoring the legislation I copied and organized.

"Jeremy," Senator Kulick commanded soon after the meeting adjourned.

"Yes, Senator?" He was rifling through his binder looking hard for something.

"Boy, where's my copy of the family law bill we discussed today?"

Knowing full well that I didn't put it in there, and despite being addressed as something only Hammer Mike had the right to call me, I disingenuously began searching. I was set to leave early to get in a winter mountain bike ride with my new mountain biking team. Then a romantic dinner with my college sweetheart.

"Oh no!" I said, "Senator, the bill isn't in here! You're right. Oh darn, I'm so sorry." Faking a panic, I continued, "I'll run one down to your office right away."

Senator Kulick must have watched a lot of mob movies growing up as his West Virginian draw deferred to an Al Pacino-like Godfather II tone when he said, "Unacceptable. I want you to come to my office with several copies of this bill so I can discuss them with my constituents."

Playing up my fake worry, I said, "Okay. I'm so sorry, Senator. Can I do anything else to make it up to you?"

The arrogant legislator commanded, "And then I want you to bring me a cup of coffee from Wendy's and today's *Gazette*."

I got busted. I had to pay for my little prank. I fetched coffee and papers all the time. No big deal. But the crotchety old man wasn't done.

"Furthermore, from here on out, you are to come to my office at least two hours before the meeting with all bills on the agenda. And I mean *ev-er-y* day. And it wouldn't hurt to ask me if I want a cup of coffee when you do."

"But Senator, many times, I don't have everything organized by..."

Senator Kulick barked, "Boy, I don't care how you do it. But you'll find a way—if you like your job, that is."

I wasn't worried about the self-entitled legislator influencing my job. I had recently gained significant job security with senate president Earl Ray Tomblin for volunteering to develop a computer program to link his technologically challenged office to Secretary of State Joe Manchin's office for purposes of senate confirmations. Most of the other members on the committee trusted me. And above all else, I was loyal. And because I was loyal, I didn't want Senator Dipshit creating any issue for Chairman Wooton or President Tomblin. So I simply said, "Yes, Senator, of course. You got it."

At that point in my life, I was thinking about marriage, settling down in Charleston and my future as a legislative "lifer," where I would likely breeze through my career in my cubicle until I accumulated a lot of benefits and retired early. Up until that moment, I had a damn good life and I thought I was content. But deep down, I had a problem with pricks like Senator Kulick. I had too much of Hammer Mike's blood in me. If I stayed the course, I would run into many Senator Kulicks. I could see myself one day despising my job. Realizing that perhaps my life wasn't as good as I thought it was, I snapped.

Senator Kulick went back to his office and I tried to muster up the humility I needed to gather what he requested. I was too outspoken. His request for daily deliveries just wasn't possible and I wasn't going to withstand another confrontation with Senator Kulick before I popped him in the mouth.

The senate had recently begun to recycle so I would put all leftover bills into big plastic bins. When full, they were heavy and probably held the equivalent of a quarter-of-a-tree's worth of paper. I wheeled one of those overflowing bins over to Senator Kulick's office. I waved at Senator Kulick's secretary and told her I had a delivery for him. I didn't wait for permission to go back. With the bin placed strategically behind me and Senator Kulick, who was sitting at his desk, I said, "Hi Senator, I brought the bills you requested."

He replied, "Fine. It took you long enough. From now on, you're going to be quicker."

"Yes, Sir!" I then turned around and wheeled the gigantic container in front of Senator Kulick's desk and said, "Here you go, Senator!"

I pushed over the bin, dumping paper everywhere.

"That family law bill you requested is in here somewhere. Every single copy. And even copies of the bills you would never read. They're in there somewhere as well. This would be a good chance for you to catch up on all the legislation you voted on without reading."

For good measure, I hoisted the bin into the air, ensuring that all of the paper had been left.

"What the fuck are you doing?" the good senator yelled.

"Sir, how did you say you wanted your coffee again?"

Senator Kulick became speechless. As I strutted out the door, that's when I told him to go fuck himself. Passing his daily-tortured secretary, I gave her a high five and walked directly home with a satisfied smile on my face.

When I arrived at my nearby apartment, I cancelled my mountain biking and dinner plans. I worked diligently on sending out my first year law application to West Virginia University College of Law, Senator Kulick's alma mater. Then I called Hammer Mike and made him a deal.

# Chapter 5

After Hammer Mike banished me from Cleveland because I quit ASL, I arrived in Charleston around 9:30 P.M. I went to Tim and Liz Murphy's house unannounced. The Murphys have been lawyers since the 1970s. Tim was like a second father to me, and Liz, a nurturing mother. I met them while working with Tim for Chairman Wooton.

Tim and Liz treated me like a son and had encouraged me to foster my ambitions. While Hammer Mike had a brash solution for all of my life predicaments, the Murphys usually came up with the same conclusions, but only after showing me premeditated reasons.

At the Murphy home, I opened the door using the key Tim always hid for me under the rug. As I sat and waited for the Murphys to come home, I cowered thinking about the last time I was there—studying for final exams after Thanksgiving. It was a horrible time. I was overcome with anxiety from not knowing what, when, or how to study. The stress of those few days was compounded because I was approaching fall semester final exams without one completed outline, and no idea what the hell I was doing.

I had foolishly counted on Charlie's, and then Lois's study group outlines to carry me. Ultimately, I never studied in college. I was my fraternity's president, student body president, Greek Council president, and captain of the crew team. I didn't have time to go to class, let alone read and outline. I probably could have made time for studying, but I often became frustrated watching my classmates read something once and get it, while I'd have to read things three to five times before it would even begin to register.

The longer I waited for the Murphys, the more I thought about why I was in law school to begin with. I didn't want to forever be a "go 'fir." Although Senator Kulick eventually started kissing my ass once he discovered that I was favored by President Tomblin, going 'fir this and going 'fir that was not something I could live with much longer. I wanted more out of life. And Hammer Mike effectively showed me that steel hauling wasn't it.

After two hours of waiting for the Murphys and wondering, my stomach felt the same type of pain as that of a man kicked in the balls. It hurt thinking about the possibility of going back to Grundy. It really hurt thinking about what I'd be up against.

Around midnight, the Murphys pulled up to their house in Tim's beat-up Mazda. Tim was Irish and Liz was Italian, and she looked it. She was short, with dark hair and an olive skin tone. Liz was a pleasant woman who always saw the glass more than half-full. When Tim and Liz walked in after their late night out, I walked into the kitchen to greet them.

"Hi, Jeremy!" Liz said in her sweet comforting voice.

I gave Liz a soft hug and Tim greeted me with his strong Irish handshake.

Before Tim even took his shoes off, he asked, "Aren't you supposed to be studying in Grundy?"

"I almost failed out," I said, ashamed.

Liz took off her overcoat, neatly folded it over the back of a chair and said, "What do you mean *almost* failed out? ASL didn't kick you out, right?"

"No. I'm in a worse position than failing out. They placed me on academic probation."

Liz gently rubbed my arm. She looked concerned and said, "Oh, Jeremy, I'm so sorry. What are you going to do?"

Although Hammer Mike's mission for me was working and I was on the verge of deciding to return to ASL, I wanted the Murphys, who were instrumental in inspiring me to go to law school even after I received all those rejection letters, to guide my final decision. I replied to Liz, "I'm so deep into probation that it would take an academic miracle to bail me out."

Tim smirked his here-we-go-again smirk. He said, "I told you it would take an act of God for you to be accepted into law school with your LSAT score, but you stuck with it, and you got in." Liz shook her head affirmatively.

I said, "But one of my professors told me I probably wouldn't pass the bar anyway. So what's the point?"

Tim was tired and didn't have enough energy to stomach any more of my excuses. He took charge and said, "Go back. You're already set up there. Apartment, classes, books, you might as well see it through."

Liz added, "You know, Jeremy, Tim's right. You'll never forgive yourself if you don't at least try."

I trusted my dad and I trusted the Murphys. All three said go back. While I dreaded going back to Grundy, I dreaded quitting even more.

# Chapter 6

"Stop fucking around," Dennis Mensinger would always say to me during the fall semester. "You've got to put aside all of this partying and get tough!" But I chose to stay irresponsible and weak, assuming things would just somehow fall into place. Surely, I thought, the world couldn't be so cruel as to allow me to fail. But I was wrong.

Dennis had volunteered to become my mentor because of an implied obligation he had to Chairman Wooton. Dennis held my legislative analyst job for several years before he outgrew it and Chairman Wooton encouraged him to go to law school. Similar to what had happened to Dennis, when Chairman Wooton found out that twenty-four of twenty-five law schools rejected me, he made me take a day off and tour ASL. Chairman Wooton wanted me to follow in Dennis's footsteps.

Dennis was one of those people who ate, slept, and shit politics. Inspired by his work with Wooton and the judiciary committee, Dennis volunteered for several campaigns for the Democratic Party and wanted to one day run for office himself. A chronic smoker and regressing skateboarder, Dennis didn't look anything like a politician. In fact, like me, he didn't even look like a law student. We both had longer hair, but he wore campaign polo shirts and beat-up khakis to class and I wore concert baseball tees and beat-up jeans. Dennis's round glasses made him look a bit like John Lennon. My appearance was a cross between Bruce Dickenson of Iron Maiden and Lemmy Kilmister of Motörhead.

Dennis's advice to me began early in the fall semester when I told him about how I caught Portia Simmons hiding a book my Legal Process class needed for an assignment. In a hidden part of the library, I saw her wrap the book in her jacket, but later heard her tell someone in our class that she didn't know where it was. I couldn't believe how malicious she was, knowing that her comrade would continue searching for the book for hours. I was even more surprised that Dennis seemingly defended Portia's actions.

"Going to law school is like being a hungry bird trying to get a good position at a birdfeeder. You start eating until three other birds are pushing you, two birds are pecking at you, and only one bird replaces you in position to eat."

Curiously, I responded, "Come on, dude. What the hell does that mean?"

"Well, Burnside," Dennis said very matter-of-factly, "whether you get fed good enough grades to survive law school will depend on your killer instinct and interpretation of the One L lie."

"I don't get it. You've lost me."

"It's called the curve, my brother, and you'll learn to hate it."

"So what's this lie you're talking about?"

Dennis Mensinger muted the television and sat up in his recliner. He proclaimed, "One Ls hope every One L becomes a Two L, regardless of how it might affect the grading curve that every One L's life is now dependent upon. One Ls are in it together."

"Thanks Den, I see your point. Law school was designed to be dog-eat-dog. Check."

Dennis nodded and said, "Hypocrites boast the lie, idiots believe it, and fools mean it."

Not hinting at my intended sarcasm, I said, "So I guess that the game has thus begun."

Dennis stood up from the recliner, put out his cigarette, turned off the television, and leaned in over me.

"No, Jeremy," Dennis said with smoke blowing in my face from his nose and mouth, "law school can never be a game. It is the war that has begun. And you better be on the front line, with your bayonet fixed and ready to attack."

The war Dennis referred to never happened for me during the fall semester. I assumed that because Charlie was my friend he wouldn't mind drafting our outlines as I leisurely strolled through the minefields of legal learning. After Charlie exiled me from his study group and left me to die a horrible scholastic death, Lois insisted I join her All-Star platoon of all-undergraduate valedictorians. When I failed to read one of the assignments for the group because I didn't want to miss a Browns' game, they expelled me from their academic army.

In late November, in the prime of finals study time, I was on my own. My actions suggest that I chose to be alone, which led to my academic doom. Being alone wouldn't have been so bad if I hadn't made myself so lost.

If I had any chance of finding my way and surviving law school after recklessly sabotaging my fall semester chances, I realized that I had to finally embrace Dennis's fall semester advice. Going back to Grundy meant going to war.

# Chapter 7

After spending the rest of the weekend with the Murphys, I decided to take the back roads through Eastern Kentucky to get to Grundy. During the drive, I thought about how making the top 10% of my class would be the apex accomplishment of my life. For me to have any chance of making Dean's List, however, I had to transform my life wholly and hurriedly.

I'd have to immediately eliminate all distraction from my life. That meant no human contact. No television, video games, sports, or any other form of enjoyment. Starting right at that moment, I had to live for studying.

By the time I exited West Virginia, I had developed a preliminary plan for mentally exterminating all the things that distracted me the most. As I approached Hatfield and McCoy Country, I felt my hands sweat. I had to get one of the less drastic, but more complicated cleansings out of the way and I was damn nervous about the aftermath.

Dumping Lois did not end with her. I knew that breaking up with the most popular girl in our class would also mean breaking up with her vast circle of friends. I would become an enemy of the class. I would become an outcast, like Asa McCoy, who was a Union soldier killed by the ex-Confederate Logan Wildcats, once led by Devil Anse Hatfield—the event that started the famed family feud. My classmates would be the Hatfields.

That was just one complication. The most significant impediment that ending things with Lois presented was loneliness. Despite keeping me on edge about studying, Lois kept me from feeling emotionally desolate in the fall. I think that's why I kept her so close for so long. That, and she really was a loving and amazing person.

It was Sunday afternoon when I arrived at Lois's apartment in Pikeville, Kentucky. She also had just arrived and was unloading her arsenal of books and study guides. As soon as Lois saw me step out of my jeep, she ran up and hugged me tightly. She said, “We’ve been so worried about you! No one knew where you were. Your mom called your place looking for you. I told her I was worried. Then she became worried. You need to call her right away.”

“I’ll call her soon enough, Lois. Let’s go inside, I’ve got something to tell you.”

I helped Lois with her things. She claimed she had been in the library studying all day despite speaking to my mom, who only called my apartment. It didn’t matter. We went inside and she took off her coat. I left mine on. Lois was smart enough to know what was coming.

As tears began to form in her eyes, Lois said, “Just tell me you didn’t go see another woman this weekend.”

“No, of course not.”

“Then why are you doing this? Why are you breaking up with me? Tell me I’m reading you wrong.”

I held Lois’ hand and said, “I’ve realized here very lately that I’ve got to change some things about myself. I’ve got to do some things with my life that can’t involve you. I’m sorry, that’s all I want to say right now.”

Struggling for words, Lois said, “I don’t even know what you’re talking about. Who the hell did you see these last few days and what did they do with my boyfriend?”

“Lois, I care about you, but I have some soul-searching to do. You’re great, and who knows? Maybe when I find whatever it is I’m looking for, we can get back together.”

“What, are you gay or something, and this is the way you’re telling me?”

With Lois’s head dug in between my arm and chest, I continued, “All I’m saying is that the Jeremy Burnside you knew and who was your boyfriend is going away for a while.”

Lois struggled to say goodbye. I hugged her gently, kissed her forehead, and stood up. She grabbed my arm and pulled me in close to her and stared in my eyes. Lois was a persistent woman. The ravishing brunette always got what she wanted.

Not this time.

Once I pulled away, like I had flipped a switch, Lois uncharacteristically went off.

"All guys are assholes, and you're the fucking king! I hope you fail out of this place so I never have to look at you again! From the way you've been acting, my guess is that you'll be ASL's next Peter O! Fuck you!"

In my mind, Lois's rant was not only the start of a One L feud, but it was the first shot of my Appalachian War. When I drove away, I began to mentally prepare myself for the inevitable rumors about me. I knew I could handle being called gay, a cheater, loner, whatever—but I also knew I would have a hard time dealing with any more predictions that I'd be ASL's next Peter O.

# Chapter 8

Hammer Mike, had he ever met Peter O, would likely have described the disturbed immigrant's mental status as "two beers short of a six pack." Sometime around fall orientation, rumors swirled about Peter O beating his wife. The unfortunate Mrs. Odighizuwa was said to have feared for her life and moved out of the marital home. The odd part of this story was that Peter O, without a scratch, insisted that he suffered invisible injury and should go to the hospital in the stead of his battered spouse. Peter O blamed his struggles, in part, on his rural American surroundings.

The mountains in Grundy are part of the Cumberland Plateau, which is the southern-most part of the Appalachian Plateau. The best way to describe the topography of Grundy is that it is one big hollow, or what most locals refer to as a "holler." Because Grundy is cut out and sandwiched in between several steep mountains, there was never much sunlight and I don't remember ever seeing any gardens. It was obvious to me that Peter O was suffering some resulting psychological effect, perhaps a depression caused by a Vitamin D deficiency. If Grundy's lack of sunlight was still able to affect my mood after growing up in a cloudy Cleveland, I couldn't imagine what it was doing to Peter O, coming from sunny Nigeria.

I saw Peter O mostly in the library, lurking like a thief. Although I never caught him hiding books like I did Portia, Peter O would somehow leave the library with his Legal Process research complete in the time it would take him to furtively copy down the assigned case cites from someone else. I was a terrible fall semester student, but at least I didn't cheat.

Dean Sutin was said to have given Peter O somewhat of a re-start of his One L year as Peter O originally began with Dennis. Dennis knew a lot about Peter O because he sat next him in most classes during Peter O's first One L year. As I got to know Peter O for myself, Dennis would often encourage me to keep my distance from him with several stories of Peter O's bizarre past.

According to Dennis, Peter O had 25 brothers and sisters. He had been in the states since 1980. Upon his arrival, and after bouncing around the country for a few years, Peter O soon moved to my native Ohio and initially enrolled at The Ohio State University, where he didn't last long. Peter O then transferred to Central State, a historically black institution located near Dayton, Ohio.

Peter O also had lived in Portland, Oregon, where he drove metro buses. Dennis somehow found out that Peter O filed his first lawsuit in 1989 after he crashed one of his buses after a police chase. In typical Peter O fashion, he claimed that he was the victim and filed a claim for unlawful discharge. But this was just the tip of the iceberg.

During the beginning of the fall semester, near the time that Peter O allegedly beat his wife, Dennis told me that he was standing near the financial aid office when he heard Peter O go on a screaming rampage towards several ASL employees, including Vickie Keene, over his tuition. Standing out in the midst of various loud derogatory names, Peter O said that ASL would "burn."

Later in that semester, Dennis claimed that he witnessed Peter O about to attack one of the librarians. All she had been doing was vacuuming the floor. Peter O had a clenched fist and was cussing at her for no apparent reason other than making noise. Dennis said that Peter O exploded so badly that it was like he was possessed by demons instructing him to kill the librarian. But when Peter O spotted Dennis, he immediately reverted back to just being silent and creepy. Peter O said hi to Dennis and then walked away.

Dennis often told me of other stories involving the troubled Nigerian. Begging for money in class, cussing out classmates in the middle of a lecture, and going off on community members for not giving him a job—they all had the common theme of Peter O believing he deserved special treatment. Throughout the fall semester, I tried to put myself in Peter O's shoes and justify his peculiar actions:

> Peter O is probably embarrassed to ask for help, but perhaps has no choice.
>
> Peter O is scared in a town where black people are foreigners.
>
> Peter O is a victim of competition and law student haughtiness.

I gave Peter O the benefit of the doubt and occasionally helped him with such things as connecting to a printer or accessing his email. Little did I know that helping Peter O with little things would eventually cause him to demand much more out of me.

We'll need to go back in time for a moment. It was right after my last fall semester exam and I had just driven from ASL's back parking lot towards the exit. I could see Peter O through what I remembered being Grundy's first snowfall of the winter. A single sunray was following him through the gloomy clouds like a spotlight. It wasn't just his very dark skin color that made him stick out. Peter O had a vile aura about him that always alerted me of his imminent presence. He wasn't the type of person you could glance at, quickly dismiss, and then go about your business. Happening upon Peter O meant that something was going to ensue: either you were going to turn and hurry in the other direction, or he was going to confront you and pressure you into doing something for him outside of your comfort zone. That day, there was only one way out of ASL for me.

I pulled up to Peter O and rolled down the window. He walked from the front of my jeep to my driver's side.

"Jed-e-me."

"Peter, what's up? I'm trying to get out of here." I was stressed out and needed to get home before I went crazy. Hammer Mike had promised me a steak dinner and I had Browns tickets I needed to pick up. Most significantly, I thought that I had just bombed every exam and had an overwhelming urge to get drunk.

Peter said, "You are from Cleveland, right?"

"Yeah, Peter, I'm going there now. What's up, dude?"

Desperately he pleaded, more like commanded, "I need you to drive me to Cleveland so I can drive taxis and make some money for my family."

I looked at Peter O and immediately shifted the jeep out of park and put it into drive.

I said, "Hey man, sorry, I need to get the fuck out of here. If you would've given me some notice, I'm sure we could've worked something out."

As he shivered, Peter O tried to sell me on the idea. He explained that he had a friend in Cleveland that he could stay with and that I didn't need to take him to the guy's house, just drop him off somewhere convenient for me. I remembered that Dennis also told me that Peter O did, indeed, drive taxis in addition to buses before coming to Grundy, so I figured Peter O was being truthful. But it didn't matter.

"Peter, I'm not even taking Lois. She would be pissed if I took you and not her."

Lois would have killed me if I had helped Peter O, especially since I told her I'd be too busy for her to come home with me to visit. I wasn't going to be too busy—I just wasn't ready to introduce her to Marijuana Alley.

Peter O was holding on to the inside of my window frame, latching on so I couldn't leave.

"My children are hungry, please help us."

"There's just no way, Peter. I'm sorry."

His eyes instantly went from desperate to explosive. I removed Peter O's icy grip by coldly rolling up my window and said, "Sorry, dude. You'll have to find someone else to take you." But I knew there would be no one else.

As I drove away, he called out, "Why doesn't anybody want to help me? Take me! Come back!"

Peter O continued shouting, but I turned the corner in the direction of the exit and circled around to the road. He walked over to where I pulled out and stood hopelessly on the sidewalk. I heard Peter O yell, "I will remember this!"

In my rearview mirror, Peter O got smaller and smaller as the spotlight that was still on him faded, like someone was lowering the dimmer. His figure disappeared in the falling snow.

I hoped that Peter O would soon get over it. But given what had happened before Dean Lund called me up to receive my fall semester grade report, and after I startled him out of Mrs. Frehley's office before I initially quit law school, it was obvious that Peter O hated me. If Peter O wanted to kill the librarian for simply running a vacuum cleaner, I could only imagine what he wanted to do to me.

Worrying about Peter O was not something I was going to do. On that drive from Pikeville to my apartment, I also decided that I was not going to allow Lois's rant about me being "ASL's next Peter O" influence the way I was going to change my life. I knew that if I had any chance of making Dean's List, I had to do more than just train my brain to be at war. I knew that if I was going to achieve the impossible, I had to not only prepare my mind, but I had to go further. Similar to how diamonds are usually discovered deep and protected in the ground, I'd have to uncover a lot about myself to truly discover my luster.

As I got nearer to the Johnson Building and closer to the start of my new attitude, I developed this formula for hopeful success by analyzing how Peter O flunked ASL. He always appeared as if he was at war himself. Late nights in the library, isolation from his classmates—it appeared that Peter O was somewhat motivated to become a Two L. But in addition to failing to put in the type of effort he needed to pass, Peter O ultimately lacked inner strength.

# Chapter 9

In 1994, during my sophomore year of high school and for the first time in my life, I dug deep into my soul to unleash a supernatural mettle. I had needed this metaphysical fortitude to make weight for a wrestling tournament one weekend. The competition had been cancelled earlier in the week due to a bad snowstorm. On Friday, however, my coach called me out of class and made me step on the scale. He always had an eye for knowing when his wrestlers were overweight. He told me the tournament was back on, but we had a three-pound cushion. After my coach moved the slider more and more to the right, the scale finally balanced at 114 pounds. Eleven pounds over 103, but only eight greater than the adjusted weight class.

My coach was furious and told me that it would be impossible for me to drop that much weight in one night. Based on his years and years of wrestling experience and the fact that I maybe had four percent body fat, my coach was absolutely certain it could not be done. While I respected him, I wasn't entirely fond of my coach and proudly imagined the embarrassed look on his face if I proved him wrong.

I skipped classes for the rest of that day and spent the next five hours wrapped in garbage bags running the halls, trying to lose as much water weight as possible. When I left the wrestling room later that evening, I had only made it to 111, still five pounds away. My mom forbade any weight loss so that night, after she went to sleep, I donned more garbage bags, several layers of clothing and ran—and ran.

The Cleveland lake effect snowdrifts were so high I had to lift my knees to my chest to stride. Mentally, I was at a place I had never been before. My body was so tired and weak that I could have lunged into the snow and fallen asleep in seconds. But something inside me kept pushing me. Was losing eight pounds over one night impossible? Had it been done before? Perhaps it happens frequently to the guys wrestling the heavier weight classes, but for a dude who was literally skin and bones? I don't know if it was adrenaline, some type of super-endorphin, or pure lunacy, but I ran all night long without a nibble or drink.

At weigh-ins shortly before the tournament began, it was my astonished coach who announced to the referee that my weight was "106." Then after winning my way to the semifinals, I drew the top seed, an undefeated phenom from a prosperous suburb. But, due to my obvious level of exhaustion, if I had any chance at winning, I would have to go back to the place in my psyche where I was the night before.

Less than twenty seconds after the whistle blew, I pinned the brute with every last ounce of energy I had. As the referee hoisted my arm, I looked over at my coach. He was flabbergasted.

I learned a lot about myself from that defining night in Cleveland. It would have been physically easy for me to not make weight and to have just witnessed the tournament from the stands. But mentally I would have watched my competition beat up on each other while wondering how I would have done if I toed the line on the mat myself. Psychologically, I would have suffered a pain more excruciating than what I experienced by choosing to lose the weight.

Legendary U.S. Supreme Court Justice Louis Brandeis once said, "Most of the things worth doing in the world had been declared impossible before they were done." From wrestling, I learned that tapping into one's vital force could sometimes be the difference in attaining the unattainable or not. In order for me to achieve the impossible in law school, I would have to again summon that same vigor on a daily basis. The semester would seem like an eternity—maybe because whatever happened in that time really was.

A vision quest is a Native-American rite of passage, where males, and sometimes females, would go on a journey to find their vision, or spiritual turning point that would allow them to discover their life direction. Losing weight for wrestling—and the 1985 Matthew Modine movie about a high school wrestler like me—made me feel like I had already experienced one. After I read more about them outside of the movies, however, I realized that vision quests were much more than just quick, emotional stimulants.

As I began my fight that spring semester at ASL, my academic and internal misgivings overwhelmed and complicated each other. To satisfy these personal qualms and bring them into harmony, I had to find my place in the circle of life.

Going deep into the belly of my essence to find clearer forms of introspection, or distinctive evaluations of my own thoughts and feelings, could only be accomplished with a spiritual vision quest.

Different ancient tribes had different vigorous rituals for the quest. Some permitted women, some only men or boys of a certain age. Some tribes required nakedness, and food and water deprivation. But all emphasized isolation and the importance of discovering one's totem, or animal messenger, which communicates one's vision from the Creator. During the vision quest, the quester used tobacco and other stimulants to clear their mind so that the vision could be attained.

A vision quest is something that can only work if the questers give everything for the sake of finding themselves. Although I wouldn't be giving up food or water or living in isolation in the forest, I accepted that I would have to give up everything that caused me pleasure and distraction to feel secluded. It was the only way.

I was lucky that ASL was located so far from civilization. There were no concerts nearby, no professional sports teams to take my money and time, and most importantly, no bars for at least an hour. Although I loved living in the Johnson Building because it was walking distance from ASL, and though I could have used the law library for purposes other than fulfilling sexual fantasies, I realized that keeping roommates would invite temptation. I had to move out.

After breaking the news to Lois and arriving in Grundy, I greeted Dennis and Tater. I informed them of my plans. Dennis said, "I'm surprised you even came back. But you gotta do what you gotta do. Since you're back, I need to talk to you later about something I should've told you last semester."

"Yeah, sure."

I looked at Tater. He didn't say a word. He knew what was happening. During my forty-five minute drive from Pikeville to Grundy, I was certain Lois called Tater to inform him of the break-up. Before Lois and I started dating, Tater told me he liked her, but he never made a move. After Tater wimped out and Lois and I dated, she spent many nights with me at the Johnson Building. I always noticed a spark between them. With me out of the picture, this was Tater's chance to finally make a play at Lois Stanley. I obviously didn't want to be around for that.

Becoming cloaked from the outside world was my goal. Although I would have preferred to live in a cave, I soon ventured to ASL and picked up a list of apartments from the admissions office. Regina Sweeny guided me to a place located above the town beauty academy and across from the flood control project. She advised me that its former tenant, one of the Failed Five, told her that it was dark, musty, and very hard to find. It sounded perfect.

When I left the office, Regina, who I had felt was on edge since we came back from break, wished me luck and gave me a half smile. This was odd because she was a full-smile-kinda-gal. I saw Nancy Pruitt walk towards the reception area, but then changed course after she and I made eye contact.

Something was up.

Soon after that thought crossed my mind, Peter O opened the door. He was walking into admissions as I was walking out. His no-nonsense demeanor signaled that he was on a mission. I tried to avoid him the best I could. I put my head down and slid my body through the door after he barged in.

"Oh, hey Peter," I reluctantly said. I thought I heard him mumble, "Fuck you" but I didn't want to stick around to find out for sure. After all, my vision quest had begun and I wasn't going to allow some asshole disturb my search to find my place in the circle.

# Chapter 10

It was January 14, 2002, and whether I liked it or not, I was a new man. In just three days, I discovered I was deep in probation, quit on my dreams, ventured home, was turned away, re-engaged my law school ambitions, broke up with the hottest girl in school and finally set myself on the path to finding myself. In those few short days, I created an imaginary war in my head to stay motivated and I began a vision quest to lift me up when that motivation would run me down. I hoped that I had set the stage for a miracle.

Although I had a good plan, it was just the beginning of what was going to be a long, difficult journey. But it had to begin at some point. So like jumping in to an ice-cold swimming pool to officially kick off summer, I delved into an unopened casebook to finally engage the spring semester assignments.

My Contracts book looked almost brand-new and crackled when I tugged the binding early that Monday morning before class. During the fall semester, I had no interest in that type of law, so I rarely gave the book much attention. Not even the salt-of-the-earth personality of Professor Tom Blackwell could breathe excitement into the principles of offer and acceptance and the dozens of rules and exceptions we had to learn about each. Contracts II, the sequel to Contracts I, promised to be equally mind-numbing. But as it was my worst fall semester grade and worth more credits than most of my other classes, understanding contracts was my key to making Dean's List. If I could turn my fall semester D into a spring semester B+, I had a chance.

My hope of making Dean's List rested on the presumption that Professor Blackwell didn't care about how much of the law we actually knew. He told us that he cared mainly about how we communicated. As such, we could score points even if our answer was wrong, but our issue spotting and analysis were right. To Professor Blackwell, thinking like a lawyer was more important than accurate rule regurgitation.

If I could learn to think like a lawyer, I could gain the assuredness and savvy of an accomplished scholar when it came time to author my exam answers. Even without Professor Blackwell saying so, specifically, it was the best thing I learned from him.

Because I waited to read any assignments until grades came out, I was five assignments behind in each class. To catch up, I had to fit into my brain as much law in one day as possible, all days. I had to efficiently keep information flowing in during most of the 1,440 minutes that exist in each of these days.

And then I had to remember it.

After it took me two hours to read only half of the very first Contracts II assignment, I knew I needed time: time to read, time to memorize, time to analyze and time to regurgitate. There didn't seem to be enough hours in a day. But somehow, I felt, there had to be a way.

While sitting in Contracts class that morning, I scribbled my "war plan" on the back of Professor Blackwell's syllabus:

| | |
|---|---|
| 5:30 A.M. to 5:45 A.M. | Get up and start coffee. |
| 5:46 A.M. to 6:00 A.M. | Get in shower. |
| 6:01 A.M. to 6:15 A.M. | Get books together, start walking to library listening to law tapes. |
| 6:16 A.M. to 8:45 A.M. | Do reading assignment for 9:00 A.M. class. |
| 8:46 A.M. to 9:00 A.M. | Go to class/ look over notes. |
| 9:01 A.M. to 11:30 A.M. | Classes. |
| 11:31 A.M. to 11:40 A.M. | Walk to apartment for lunch listening to law tapes. |
| 11:41 A.M. to 12:00 P.M. | Make and eat lunch while going over notes. |
| 12:01 P.M. to 12:40 P.M. | Outline class notes. |
| 12:41 P.M. to 1:00 P.M. | Walk back to ASL for afternoon classes listening to law tapes. |
| 1:01 P.M. to 3:00 P.M. | Afternoon classes. |

| | |
|---|---|
| 3:01 P.M. to 6:30 P.M. | Do reading assignment for next day's mid-morning classes. |
| 6:31 P.M. to 7:50 P.M. | Make dinner and eat while looking over notes. |
| 7:51 P.M. to 8:00 P.M. | Walk to law library listening to law tapes. |
| 8:01 P.M. to 10:30 P.M. | Legal Process work/outline class notes. |
| 10:31 P.M. to 10:40 P.M. | Walk home listening to law tapes. |
| 10:41 P.M. to 11:00 P.M. | Check messages/email. |
| 11:01 P.M. | Fall asleep listening to law tapes. |

Listening to law tapes wasn't essential in terms of memorizing the material. I planned on listening to them to keep my mind on the law and to prevent my contemplations from drifting somewhere else. Following this schedule was how I was going to catch up, finally discover how to study, learn, practice, and make Dean's List.

I couldn't miss anything my professors said and therefore couldn't miss class. If I did, I knew that I might miss the one rule that would make the difference from being a Two L and being a truck driver. I stopped using my laptop in class, which meant no more instant messaging, email, or online chess. After all, I was .06 away from being checkmated.

⚖

After that pivotal first day back, I woke up according to the time in my new war plan. I made it to the library on time and was the first one there. I walked straight to an open study carrel, sat down and began reading that day's Criminal Law assignment. I read the assignment, went to class, and paid attention.

After Criminal Law was over, I checked my mailbox before preparing to go upstairs to announce to Mrs. Frehley that I was back. I found a memorandum from Dean Sutin that I had received a week prior, setting forth the rules of my probation. I must have dropped it while I was in a panic the day I initially quit. Someone must have picked it up from the mailroom floor and placed it back in my box. My academic secret was probably out.

Everyone would soon know, if they didn't already.

When I walked down the hall leading to Mrs. Frehley's office, she saw me as she was making what seemed to be an abrupt exit. She hid her face and said, "Glad to see you, Jeremy. I've got to run, sorry."

As she quickly walked away, it appeared as if Mrs. Frehley had been crying or had recently been frightened. At about the same time I noticed this, I saw Peter O leave her office, upset and talking to himself.

Why did he keep coming to Mrs. Frehley's office? Peter O was definitely trying to intimidate her into changing his grade or something.

I had other things to worry about other than Peter O's strange actions. For the remainder of the day, I wondered who found out about me being on probation and how quickly the word would spread. I was distracted.

Distraction would equal Ds.

I had to find a way to stop the speculation. It was killing some of the minutes designated for study.

I had to think—I had to think about law.

I spent lunchtime trying to cram in the most recent Contracts II assignment, still scratching the surface of what I had missed. I simply highlighted issues I thought Professor Blackwell would feel important. In the end, being a law student also meant you had to employ some form of mind reading.

Professor Blackwell's method of choosing students to call on involved a few decks of playing cards, each card marked with a name. He picked several cards throughout the day. Charlie and I previously dubbed it, "The Blackwellic Method." Due to the difficulty of the subject matter, my classmates and I would mentally gasp after every shuffle and selection. In Contracts, we were ever so conscious of the negative stigma a law student receives after bumbling in class.

That day, I had a feeling I was about to be called on. My intuition was correct as Professor Blackwell shouted, "Lucky Ace of Spades. Looks like today's ace is... Jeremy Burnside."

I confidently lifted my hand in the air.

"Over here, Professor."

Professor Blackwell scanned the room a few times until he located me in the center back. "Mister Burnside," he said, "tell the class about the effect drunkenness has on the formulation of an enforceable contract."

Drunkenness.

Is he kidding me?

"Yes, sir." I took a deep breath, trying to suppress my worry.

Come on Jeremy, just answer the damn question!

As I hesitated, Professor Blackwell grew impatient. He said, "We're waiting, Mister Burnside."

I scanned the highlighted portions of my book and took one helluva deep breath.

The issue is drunkenness, so just give him the rule.

"Pursuant to *Martin v. Harsh*, drunkenness cannot be used as an excuse to drown out someone's mental state in making decisions...

He likes context, so find something.

Ah!

"To add context, in *Lucy v. Zehmer*, the court determined that the defendant was not intoxicated enough in that case to not know the nature of his instrument."

The tenacious Texan struck back with a question regarding a different issue. My paranoia about him knowing about my drunkenness during his exam thankfully disappeared. "What about contracts with minors?" he asked.

I thought I saw that, but where did it go?

Found it. Yes!

"Contracts with minors are voidable. In the 1970s, the age determination of who is a minor dropped from 21 to 18 because of the voting age. A contract can be found not to be voidable, however, if it involves a necessity, such as an educational loan or housing."

"Very good, Ace. Way to be prepared."

Sweet!

After Professor Blackwell picked the next playing card in the deck, I sat back and thought about the academic progress I made in just one day, by simply following my new war plan. During the fall semester, I would have frozen, certainly bumbled, and looked like an idiot. Although I wasn't as prepared as I needed to be, I sounded like I knew what I was talking about.

I can do this.

If for only that moment, Dean's List didn't seem so impenetrable.

# Chapter 11

After Contracts was over, I drove to the local YMCA, ready to clear my head. With my classmates littered throughout the weight room, and while wearing my tight crew unisuit from college, I spent some time yanking the oar handle on the rowing machine. The Y's only ergometer had a TV screen attached to it with these Atari-looking rower dudes racing each other. I had put on some weight since my last college crew season, but the exercise felt good as the familiar motions of rowing relaxed my mind. I was on calm waters, rowing with the current, surrounded by beauty and as my little rower guy on the screen indicated, I was enjoying a commanding lead.

After that first workout, I felt refreshed. I took a shower and drove down the street back to ASL to continue my intense catch-up. As the evening wore on, and everyone began to leave the library, I was losing steam. My eyes wandered away from my books. I frequently gazed outside and finally had to crack a window to stay awake. As I opened the window, I heard a vehicle start. I thought everyone was gone and looked to see who it was.

It was Professor Blackwell. He must have been working late. I looked back at my Civil Procedure book and tried to read some more. I could still hear Professor Blackwell's truck running outside. I peered out. I saw Peter O get in.

Interesting.

When I arrived at the Johnson Building late that evening, on what was supposed to be my final night as a tenant there, Tater was talking on the cordless phone in his room, no doubt to Lois. He didn't look at me through the doorway when I glanced in. I walked over to the kitchen, where Dennis was eating a bowl of cereal.

"Hey Dennis," I said, looking for a beer in the fridge. "I saw Peter O get a ride from Professor Blackwell a little bit earlier."

"That's odd," Dennis replied with milk dribbling down his chin through the hairs of his goatee. “There’ve been sightings of him all around campus. I thought he failed out. I’m still waiting for him to go postal.”

“Dude,” I said, shuffling things around in the fridge. “Peter O is harmless. He’s probably just stuck here with nowhere to go. Professor Blackwell was probably taking him to a bus station or something.”

“In Grundy?”

“True. But if there was a professor that would drive Peter O to a distant bus station, other than Dean Sutin, it’d be Tom.”

I gave up on my beer search and started walking to my room when Dennis tried to stop me.

“Hey Jeremy, now’s a good time to discuss what I’ve been meaning to tell you…

I interrupted and said, “Sorry, Den. I have to get to bed. I’m probably moving out tomorrow. Good night.”

“Hey, wait!”

I wasn’t in the mood to get into what I figured was going to be a deep conversation with Dennis. When I got to my room and closed my door, I changed my clothes and sat at my desk. I looked at the rejection letters remaining on my wall that I did not previously rip down.

Sacramento University.

William and Mary.

West Virginia University.

Out of nowhere, and despite a very productive day, I instantly became depressed. I got in bed and pulled my blanket over my head. Keeping the pace I set seemed too difficult and the end of the semester seemed so far away.

How am I supposed to keep this up for nearly four more months?

Sleep became unattainable as my heart raced with uneasiness. I couldn’t control my thoughts.

Top 10% in the class?

All Bs?

At least one B+?

An A?

On ASL's bell curve?

With no help?

Shit! Shit! Shit!

In that moment, I didn't think I could ever erase my fall semester blunders. I was buried up to my chin in reading and outlining. Money was going to run out well before the end of the semester. I had no one to support me. It was the first time in my life that I felt that the future was totally out of my control.

In laymen's terms, I was freaking the fuck out.

Even after the two previous days of positive momentum, I felt like I was losing my mind. The pressure I felt when deciding whether to quit law school altogether was magnified. Making Dean's List was, indeed, impossible. I couldn't bring myself back to that place in my mind where I was motivated.

Finally, after sparring with my thoughts for what seemed like hours, I decided that I had choices to make: find a way to end my anguish or lose control. Persevere or secede. Or, per my war-like mindset, kill or be killed.

I somehow decided I needed a sign that I could stay alive in my quest. Impatient and emotionally broken, I prayed. I prayed for the first time since September 11. In my head I whispered my request for a vision of what I should do repeatedly as if it were a lullaby.

Please show me, Lord…

Tomorrow please give me a sign of what I should do.

Please show me, Lord.

The next thing I knew, it was morning, and I had a fresh new day. I woke up and looked out my window.

If my prayers are answered, there'll be a revelation and I'll find myself—today.

# Chapter 12

On January 16, 2002, I awoke confident that God would send me my vision, or at least some spiritual signal to show me how I could accomplish the impossible. When I got to the library that morning, I was the first one there and planned to be the last one to leave in the evening. It was dark outside and the inside lights were off. The library door security card activator wasn't working so I walked to the main building to wait.

I sat alone in trial courtroom and read about venue, the place where a litigant could properly file a lawsuit. When I finished, I walked outside and waited for my sign in the Lion's Lounge, which lobby-like area was guarded by two carved-out wooden lions.

Lions are often totems, or animal messengers in vision quests.

Maybe these lions are mine.

I sat and watched people filter into the school. One by one, One Ls, Two Ls, and Three Ls alike entered the building. Many seemed stressed and ragged. Others probably thought they were doing a good job pretending that they were as eager as they were in the fall. During the cold winter months of law school, ASL's once ambitious and enthusiastic first-year students had succumbed to apathy and lethargy. Not even the Lois Stanleys of the class were impervious to law school's undocumented tutorials on humility.

Angela Dales, a hard-working single mother who had gone from ASL admissions counselor to One L, strolled through the doors ready to take on the day. Professor Blackwell held the door for her. Angela was well respected in our class for her bravery in leaving her admissions job to pursue an expensive dream. While watching Angela in the Lion's Lounge that day, it didn't seem like her ambition was as obvious as it usually was—perhaps because she was tired, or maybe she didn't read for our next class.

At about the same time Angela entered ASL that chilly morning, Dennis

Mensinger walked over, sat down next to me, and shook his head. He joined in my gaze and said, "She's really something, huh?"

"Yeah, she's pretty awesome."

Although speaking with Dennis was technically a violation of my "no distractions" code, I felt comforted. We continued to chat when Dean Sutin walked in. The fact that Sutin was our law school dean still baffled me.

Dean Sutin was like a hall-of-fame coach leading the worst team in the league. He had served as Deputy Director of the U.S. Department of Justice's "COPS" program, a program that he helped write legislation to create, was counsel to President Clinton, an Assistant U.S. Attorney General—the list went on and on. But somehow, someway, ASL scored him. Dean Sutin's professional successes mirrored his personal ones, making him that much more special.

Dennis said, "He and his wife just brought home their new adopted child. Her name is Clara Li. Dean Sutin is on Cloud Nine right now, and if you saw Clara Li, you'd understand why."

"Oh, who's his wife? How does she stay busy in Grundy? Culture shock for her?"

Dennis's initial puzzled look changed to downright bewilderment.

"Damn, buddy, no wonder you're on probation. You weren't even here last semester! His wife is Margaret La . . ."

An imaginary light bulb lit up over my head.

"Oh! Professor Lawton! She teaches trial tactics. I spoke to her once. She's a nice lady."

"She is." Dennis said, "I have her this semester."

Suddenly, Dennis got quiet. His calming, pleasant nature got tough and firm. In the short amount of time since I began my daily war plan, I sometimes saw Dennis up late at night in his recliner when I would get back from the library. He'd say hi and sit up in the chair like he wanted to talk. But each time this happened, I just ignored him and quickly closed my bedroom door. I was afraid he'd question why I came back so I avoided him. While sitting in the Lion's Lounge that day, Dennis finally took the opportunity to get whatever it was he wanted to say off his chest.

"Now listen. Ever since you told me you were on probation, there's been something I've been meaning to tell you."

"Oh? When you told me that there's no way I could pass this semester? When you told me that it's impossible?" I said.

"Well, I guess I should've prefaced my answers with what I'm about to say. It's not that I think it's totally impossible. Actually, I think it's quite possible. I told you that because I didn't think you had what it takes to go above what I did."

Still upset, I quipped, "What you did? I don't have what it takes to do what you did? What is it that *you* did, Den?"

Dennis paused and sat up straight. He said, "Dean Sutin placed me on academic probation after my first fall semester. I had a 1.89. After my second semester, my grades improved, but I fell short of the required 2.0 by a .02 difference. I petitioned the school to let me back in."

I sat shocked.

"Okay, you mean to tell me that you went on probation, then actually failed out completely and now you're a Two L?"

"Yes, and after last semester, I'm now in good standing. But Jeremy, you have to understand that my GPA of 1.89 was close to two letter grades better than what you're dealing with now. I didn't want to see you go through the emotional anxiety that I did. For you, attempting to become a Two L might not be worth it."

Half-seriously, half-sarcastically, I said, "Was it worth it for you, Den?"

"Maybe. Sometimes I wonder. I lost my wife to divorce because of Grundy's lack of bustle. At times, knowing I was failing out, I lost my mind. That whole year of my life, ruined. My wife didn't think I could make it with the grades I had. She gave me an ultimatum to quit and I didn't. Sometimes I wish I did. She'd still be with me. I'd be back in Charleston, working for Chairman Wooton, a happier person."

My hovering angst towards Dennis about his doubt in me had withered. I said, "Wow. What a story. I guess I don't have as much to lose. But I've been so disturbed about this."

"No, you don't have as much to lose. And now the more I think about it, that's the reason you should try to do this. I'm not going to lie and say you have a great chance of accomplishing Dean's List, but think about if you did. I only had to make up .11 to pass. You have .27 to go. That could maybe be a record or something. By coming back here facing those odds, you're showing me that you're crazy. But in order to do what you need to, you have to be."

"Crazy… It sure would be something, all right."

"Granted, others may look at your face and think you're nuts. I'll know you're just hungry."

"Thanks, Den. Really. This was just what I needed. Exactly what I needed. This might sound silly, but I prayed for this conversation last night. And those wooden lions over there, they're totems. It's a long story."

I noticed from the corner of my eye that the room was clearing out. Classes were about to begin. I shook Dennis's hand and thanked him again.

My vision.

Thank you, Lord.

⚖

I rushed over to the trial courtroom and barely snuck in the door before Dickey Eisen closed it for the start of Civil Procedure. The seat I picked for the spring semester was in the second row, center, as opposed to the back corner during the fall semester when I hid to play online chess. During every class for the rest of the year, I wanted to remind Dickey that I wasn't quitting, as he suggested. I wanted to show him that he was wrong about me not belonging in law school. I wanted him to know that he could not intimidate me.

When class was over, I had three hours before Property II was to begin. Before I left, I said a few prayers to thank God for answering my request from the prior evening. I walked out of the trial courtroom and headed straight to the library. I planned on skipping lunch and wanted to get as caught up as I could and possibly still read that day's assignment. As I walked through the Lion's Lounge, I thought I saw Peter O walk upstairs.

There he is again.

When I got to the library, I noticed that most of the study booths were occupied. I went straight to the carrel in which I sat the prior evening. I read quickly, almost to a skim, and summarized the different case rules on my legal pad. My pens were burning up the pages and my right leg was twitching two hundred beats per minute, signaling that my mind was running on all cylinders.

As I cranked out more and more notes, Property II got closer and closer. Before I knew it, I became totally caught up in all delinquent Property readings and was about to start the first case of that day's assignment. I looked down at my watch. 1:15 P.M.

Sweet. I've got fifteen minutes to either wait in the Lion's Lounge, or I can keep on reading here.

Without giving myself much of a choice, I opened my book to *Murray Drive-In Theater v. Kirkpatrick*. It was a 1953 Indiana case about a plaintiff who signed a lease to rent land to use as a drive-in movie theatre. After I read the case, I began writing the case caption on a new page in my legal pad. I was excited about how my writing looked. I had to make my chicken scratch more legible to my professors. To practice, I used a new script in all CAPS, which caused me to slow down. To aid with my retention levels, I used different colored inks and included highlighting for major points.

As I continued to write my notes, I smiled. At that moment, I had no doubt that my decision to return to Grundy was just. I had no doubt that I had a chance.

Dean's List, here I come!

As I got about halfway through my *Murray Drive-In Theater* notes, I looked down at my watch. 1:20 P.M. I had eight more minutes to write as many notes about the case as I could and then run to class. It was a good plan. God had another.

Someone screamed, "Get out of here! Run! He's coming this way!"

It was Dennis. He was running through the library bellowing at the top of his lungs.

"Hurry, get out! He's coming! Can we lock the doors? Help! Hide! Run!"

I sat there shocked in the study carrel with my books open. Bluggton Wayne Carr was sitting behind me. He shuffled over and said, "Hey City, what the hell is goern' on in hair?"

"How should I know?"

Trying to control my own pulse before confusion completely overwhelmed me, I took a deep breath and said to Blugg, "Let me see if I can find Dennis."

I briskly walked towards the circulation desk and began to see people jumping behind desks and grasping onto things like they needed them as weapons.

"Does anyone know what's going on? Does anyone know what Dennis is yelling about?" I shouted.

I could still hear Dennis, who by that point had made his way upstairs. I stood motionless, and I tried to allow my brain time to process what was going on around me before I completely flipped out.

As Dennis ran back down the stairs, I stopped him momentarily by grabbing his shirt.

"Dennis, what the fuck is going on?"

He hardly acknowledged my existence and yelled down the hallway, "He's got a gun! He's already killed people! Run! Out the back!"

Dennis then broke my grip, ran towards the back of the library, and disappeared.

At this point, everything was going in slow motion. I was seeing the motions of people scurrying under tables, crouching behind counters—all frame-by-frame. Blugg, the tough redneck, crouched behind shelves of books. A few of my classmates escaped out of the first floor windows and were running through the parking lot away from campus. I roared, "Someone needs to lock these doors. The card reader is broke so it won't unlock the doors. Lock them so no one can get in!"

As the pandemonium was taking place, I looked out the nearest window to cars parked in the back lots and saw one of my classmates with a gun, heading towards the doors.

Is this who Dennis was yelling about?

"Someone lock these fucking doors!"

Then life got even slower, like the batteries in my brain were dying. Despite my need for reaction, I stood stationary. Thoughts traveled through my mind as fast as pouring molasses.

I closed my eyes and took a breath. When I opened them, everything around me suddenly switched into hyper-speed. My heart abruptly started to race. My eyes obsessively scanned the area around me. My obsession with locking the library doors willed me to them as I thought I might have been able to manually lock them. Without success, I frantically peeked out one of the doors' narrow windows.

Peter O was walking out of the Lion's Lounge. His hands were in the air. The armed classmate pointed a gun at him.

Focused for a moment, my eyes told my brain what they thought was occurring.

He's going to shoot Peter O!

No!

Another person converged on Peter O with another gun. The Nigerian appeared confused.

There are two gunmen?

Is this fucking Columbine, all over?

The gunmen kept their guns pointed at Peter O as a bystander close to the ASL Lion's Lounge entrance bum-rushed Peter O and tackled him to the ground. More people followed the man's crushing lead. I couldn't figure out what was going on. Everything was still happening so fast.

Once I saw Peter O's body slam against the ground, I ran towards the back of the library to look for Dennis. He was nowhere to be found. I then ran to the top of the stairs on the second floor to see if everyone was okay. Finally, I ran back to where my books were and packed them in my bag, put on my coat and stopped. I stopped dead in my tracks.

Where the hell am I going? What am I doing?

That burst of energy was short lived. After I prepared myself to make a quick exit out the back, I felt a sense of helplessness take over my body. My body and brain shut down at the sight of one of our classmates, Rebecca Brown, being helped into the library. I saw that she had a gunshot wound in her shoulder area and was bleeding. At that point, Rebecca Brown seemed more embarrassed than worried about actually being shot. Her face was red.

Rebecca said, "That idiot shot me!"

Although Rebecca seemed initially angry, that anger soon wore off. She realized the graveness of her circumstance. Library staff members were tending to her.

I heard Rebecca yell, “I need a tourniquet. Can someone get me a tourniquet?”

Not taking my eyes off what was happening in the library staff area, I reached down to my belt. I was wearing my rowing strap belt, which was comprised of strong material used to tighten crew boats for transport. It was perfect for a tourniquet. I began to loosen it slowly. I started to take it out of my belt loops. I wanted to help Rebecca. I wanted to do something. I took a step with my belt in my hand. Then I stopped. I tried to take another step, but my body again froze. I just stood and watched. I couldn’t move.

Are there two gunmen terrorizing ASL?

What should I do?

Did they shoot Peter O?

Should I go and see what’s going on outside?

I hope Rebecca is okay.

I wanted to run and give my belt to Rebecca. I wanted to run to the Johnson Building and get my jeep to rush Rebecca to the hospital down Slate Creek. I wanted to check on the others who Dennis claimed were shot. But I did nothing. Unable to mentally pull my belt completely off, I just shut down.

After a few minutes of thinking of nothing, and after others tended to Rebecca in my stead, I finally was able to collect myself. Suddenly needing a change of scenery, I grabbed my backpack and opened the library doors. As I did, it was as if I was opening the gates of hell.

I took a few uneasy strides down to the parking lot then paused. Everywhere I looked seemed to have fuzzy matting around the borders of my vision. It was as if I was watching a television show where a character was dreaming. Something then came over me. I somehow floated towards the Lion’s Lounge. As I tried to enter through a side door, I was bumped by several distressed people trying to get out.

“No, no, no!” One older Three L yelled as she pushed me. “This can’t be happening!”

A One L covered in blood followed behind the tormented Three L. The One L yelled, “Please don’t die, Stacey!”

I gave up trying to enter the Lion’s Lounge. I peered through one of the narrow doors that lined the wall opposite of the old wooden lion carvings. Stacey Beans, my classmate from Kentucky, was lying on the floor with people surrounding her. One of those people yelled in frustration, "We need an ambulance! Help!"

I had imagined those wooden lions keeping the Lion's Lounge safe. They were proud and strong. Their eyes focused on the doors, ready to attack any intruder. But that day the lions failed.

I peered in closer and could see different groups of people huddled around what appeared to be two other people down. Everyone seemed to have been screaming for ambulances. The fact that at least ten minutes had passed and no ambulances had yet arrived infuriated me and caused me to yell into the air.

"Where are the fucking ambulances?"

"What the fuck!"

As I walked towards the lawn where the others had plastered Peter O to the ground, I heard the Nigerian mumbling. I couldn't make out what he was saying, but as I got closer, I began to realize what he had done.

From the beginning of the school year, Dennis said Peter O would go postal.

Dennis was right again.

I stepped from the parking lot to the sidewalk and got an even closer look. I thought I heard some of Peter O's words. I thought I heard him mutter, "I have nowhere to go! I didn't take my medication."

The police finally converged on the scene. Their knees pulverized Peter's ribs. His head was crushed into the cold January grass. The authorities picked him up by the handcuffs and hauled him away. I stood and watched as the cop cruiser whisked Peter from ASL and presumably the outside world for the rest of forever.

ASL collectively exhaled. After a few moments, ASL staff, faculty, and students began to gather in the parking lot between the Lion's Lounge and the library. They came from the library, the Lion's Lounge, in between cars, or any other place they could have hidden. I saw Lois and she saw me. We rushed towards each other and hugged. As tears ran down her face, Lois looked at me. She tried to speak. After a few deep-breathed stammers, Lois finally was able to say, "Why did he do this?"

While Lois cried on my shoulder, I saw Dennis walking out of the Lion's Lounge doors, repeatedly shaking his head. Speaking to him earlier that day was supposed to be my vision, my sign, that my presence in Grundy was spiritually proper. As bedlam surrounded me, however, I very selfishly couldn't help but to wonder whether I was being punished.

# Chapter 13

"I don't know why Peter did this," I lied to Lois. I thought I knew damn well why. "But he will surely rot in hell." We held each other until Lois built up enough strength to wipe her eyes.

"I can't believe this is happening. It was just supposed to be another boring Property class," she said.

"Hopefully everyone will be okay. We'll all get through this."

I let go of Lois and kissed her on the cheek. A comforting peck from familiar lips. She walked over to Portia Simmons, who had blood on her shirt, but not before looking back at me, as if Lois was telling me that she didn't want me to let her go.

From the extent of Portia's panic, my optimism that everyone would recover quickly vanished. Things were very grim in the Lion's Lounge. Portia's body was shaking, but her face was catatonic.

I found Charlie Vincent and asked, "Did anyone die?" I wasn't sure I wanted to know the answer, but I had to ask.

"I can't say for sure, but a few people are tending to Dean Sutin and Professor Blackwell upstairs now. But I think they're both gone."

"What?"

Bullshit.

This can't be. Dean Sutin, Professor Blackwell. Dead?

"Are you sure, man?" I asked.

Charlie replied, "I was fucking waiting to talk to Professor Eisen about the assignment on venue when that mutherfucker went into Blackwell's office."

"Peter O, right?"

"No, fucking Santa Claus—of course him, jerk-off."

All of a sudden, Charlie placed his face in his trembling hands and began to cry. In a voice thicker than his normal Jersey accent, Charlie sobbed, "I heard gunshots then a secretary scream. Then I heard Sutin's secretary down the hall. I got the fuck outta there."

I had experienced at least sixty different emotions in the twelve to fifteen minutes between Dennis dashing through the library and Charlie telling me about the situation upstairs. Confusion, hope, disenchantment, anger—it was like my emotions were staggering over each other. It was hard to talk. I again felt an overwhelming weakness extend through my body, but still tried to stay optimistic.

Well, maybe with the Lord's goodness, they can be saved. Maybe if the damn ambulances would get here, all of them can be saved!

Charlie left with the aid of Madison St. John, our former study group partner and good friend. This was 9/11 all over for Charlie. He was even wearing the same beat-up Jets polo shirt he had on when he discovered his cousins didn't get out of Tower 1. I yelled at a staff member walking aimlessly.

"Hey, has anyone heard about how Dean Sutin and Professor Blackwell are doing?" She ignored me and the fact that she was missing a shoe.

After about two minutes of searching for answers, I saw Dennis sitting on a nearby curb. His eyes were aimed at the ground and his fingers clenched tightly together as he tried to rock himself. I walked over to him and sat down. I placed my arm around him.

"Den, are you okay?" I startled him.

Dennis jumped, realized who it was and shivered like he was naked in the arctic.

Dennis mustered the words, "They—they—they can't die! Why has this happened? There must have been something I could've done."

"What happened in there?"

Dennis took a deep breath and looked over at me with his bloodshot eyes.

"I was upstairs when it happened. I was in Mrs. Frehley's office. She's been tutoring me on how to work on my answers for exams. It was a condition Dean Sutin made me follow in order to come back to ASL after my petition."

Dennis stopped, wiped off his eyes, and sniffed the snot back into his nose. He stuttered, "I . . . I was in Mrs. Frehley's office when I noticed her face swell up with horror. She saw Peter O walking down the hall and quickly had me close and lock the door so he wouldn't see us. She was scared of him because of some threats he had made or something. A few seconds later, I heard a scary knock and a voice from the other side say, 'I need to talk to you, open the door. Now!'"

Dennis stopped his story. We both looked up. Someone had backed a station wagon to one of the opened narrow Lion's Lounge side doors. A few students were loading Stacey Beans inside. Dennis continued as if he was pretending he didn't see Stacey being hoisted into the car. He was starting to regain some composure.

"It was Peter O on the other side of the door. I could sense that Mrs. Frehley was terrified so I stayed quiet. We waited in silence with the door closed for about five minutes until Mrs. Frehley was sure he was gone."

Dennis stopped his story again. We looked. The car with Stacey Beans had pulled out and a helicopter was landing in the grass in front of the library. As the propeller slowed, one medic ran into the school and another into the library. I nodded as if to say to Dennis to keep going.

"I walked Mrs. Frehley to her car; down the stairs at the end of the hall, out the doors by Food City. After I walked back up the stairs, Peter O's voice was projecting faintly from the other end of the hall. I walked down there slowly and found out where his voice was coming from. He was in Doctor McGhee's office carrying on about why his grades were so bad and that there was some sort of conspiracy against him."

I cautiously interrupted, "Dennis, did you see a gun? Did he shoot Doctor McGhee?"

"No. I stood there only for a moment. I didn't want him to see me. Like a little pussy, I rushed into the restroom across the hall from Doctor McGhee's office area, went into a stall, hoping to avoid him. That's when I heard Doctor McGhee's door slam, then Peter O talking to himself as he walked down the hall towards the president's office. I quickly opened the stall door and heard a pop, then more. I wasn't sure what the pops were. I wished I knew what was going on."

Dennis stopped again. He looked towards the library. My eyes followed his. Paramedics wheeled Rebecca Brown out to the helicopter on a gurney.

Surely, she's okay. She was fine and pissed off when she was shot. But still, I should have given her my damn belt.

I should have done a lot of other things, too.

I turned my attention back to Dennis and said, "Go on, buddy."

When I asked him to continue, tears began to form in his eyes. He didn't want to believe what he was about to tell me. Dennis took two deep breaths and said, "As I approached Dean Sutin's office, I saw Peter O walking casually down the hall. I didn't see a gun, just him walking like nothing happened. Then I heard a loud scream. It was Dean Sutin's secretary. She was screaming at the top of her lungs. I ran inside Dean Sutin's office and there he was, keeled over, dying right there. Before I could do anything else or assist, I heard more pops, followed by more screams. Not knowing if I should stay and help Dean Sutin or run in the direction of the pops, I stood there to gather my thoughts. I never saw anyone die before. I can honestly say I pissed my pants a little."

Dennis stopped, stood up, and yelled to the undertaker already on scene, "Hey, they're upstairs. You'll need two body bags."

I encouraged Dennis to sit back down and let the authorities handle everything.

"Okay Den," I impatiently said. "Please tell me what happened next."

"Sure. But I can't talk much more about this."

"Okay, well, just leave out the details and sum everything up."

Dennis nodded.

"I decided to run in the direction of the second set of screams. It was Professor Blackwell. He was dead. I then ran back over to Dean Sutin's office. That's when I heard a group of screams downstairs in the Lion's Lounge. I also heard several pops. Terrified, I sprinted out the back doors, down the stairs by the appellate courtroom, across this parking lot, and into the library. That's about when I bumped into you. You grabbed my shirt or something. That's it."

When Dennis concluded, I tried to sob, but was still in too much shock.

I saw a van pull up to the school and heard another helicopter overhead. The media had arrived. As the mayhem continued, and more and more people from the community gathered, Doctor McGhee, our fall semester Torts professor and doctor of psychology, was the only calm person within the chaos. She came out of nowhere.

She announced, "Students, go home and tell the ones you love that you're okay.

Go on, now."

Doctor McGhee, an older Irishwoman who walked with a cane, shuffled out of the way. A stretcher with a woman's body rolled quickly out of the doors, with two people performing CPR all the way to the ambulance. It took a moment for Dennis to see what I was seeing. He quickly got up and rushed towards the ambulance.

Dennis frantically yelled, "No! Not Angela, too! Please don't die!"

I then realized the woman was Angela Dales. She had recruited Dennis to ASL when she was an admissions counselor. The two then became good friends. I quickly grabbed hold of him and prevented him from entering the ambulance. Dennis was too emotionally drained to put up a fight.

After seeing Angela Dales being taken away in the squad, I didn't know what else to do. I closed my eyes and tried to come up with a plan of action. Nothing—only guilt. When I opened my eyes, Dennis had disappeared—the guilt remained.

I needed to call my mom to let her know I was okay. It was only a matter of time before the news reports got back to her while she worked in her populated office and I didn't want her to freak out. I figured she'd call Hammer Mike after we spoke. When I arrived at the Johnson Building, I saw Dennis, who must have gotten a ride after seeing Angela. He was crying uncontrollably, with his head buried in the couch. Tater was staring at the television.

Tater had played hooky and wasn't on campus that day. He was getting his information from CNN. As Tater was witnessing everything down the road through the tube of our shared 32' Sanyo, he stayed in a deep state of disbelief. He was probably taken back to when we all watched the events of 9/11 together from the same television and with some of the same reporters. To Tater, if it was all real, it was being broadcast from far away and by familiar TV strangers. What happens on TV was supposed to be remotely isolated from Grundy—not remotely transmitted from Grundy.

Dennis kept repeating, like his brain was a record player and his needle kept skipping, "I joked that he would go postal. I joked that Peter O would go postal. I joked."

I gave Dennis another hug and tried to calm him. He kept blaming himself for what had happened. Tater took over attempting to comfort the broken Two L. I went into my room and called my mom, just like I did on 9/11.

As I dialed my mom's work number, I was immediately reminded of my frantic conversation with her when I heard that United Flight 93 was off course and near Cleveland. During the late morning of September 11, I pleaded with her to get out of the high-rise building she was working in, which is connected to the Terminal Tower, Cleveland's most recognized landmark. When my mom answered the phone on January 16, those feelings of panic returned and the events of that day started to hit me.

"Sherwin-Williams, International. May I help you?"

"Yeah, hey mom. Did you hear?"

"Hi, Jeremy. No. Hear what?"

"Do you remember that guy I told you about from my school who wanted me to give him a ride to Cleveland for Christmas Break?"

"I think I . . . remember."

"Well, he went and shot a bunch of people at my school today. I'm freaking out, mom."

"Oh my gosh! Are you kidding? Jeremy!"

As tears began to form in my eyes, I replied, "I just stood there, mom. Stood in one spot. People needed my help and I froze. I don't know what to do."

My mom said, "Jeremy, you can't think about that. Go and be there for your friends. How's Lois?"

My tears didn't break free. They just sat in the crevices of my eyes and blurred my vision. I closed my bedroom door. My heart sunk low into my belt. I forgot about my vision quest until my mom reminded me that I chose to abandon my friends for a life as a distraction-free machine, with a war plan and on a spiritual journey to find myself.

"Mom, I don't have any friends, I dumped Lois, and everyone probably thinks I'm crazy."

"Jeremy, I know you get mad when I say this, but you need to pray. When you were a kid, you used to pray. You've since forgot how much it helps. It's okay to get back to that, Jeremy. Okay?"

"Ma, lay off that church talk, okay? That's not going to help me right now. Didn't you hear me when I said there was a shooting here today?"

It aggravated me every time my mom told me to pray and go to church. I was done with the Catholic Church. My faith, or lack thereof, was my choice. No one was going to make me pray.

Disappointed in my response, my mom said, "One day you'll see what I am talking about. Can you go to Charleston tonight to clear your head?"

My mom had a good idea. I needed to get out of Grundy—again. I needed to run, to hide from the guilt that was building inside of me. After I hung up the phone, I walked back into the living room, hoping to hear some good news before I'd leave.

Charlie and Madison had arrived and were sitting on the couch watching footage of the news helicopter I saw overhead right before I ran from the school. I greeted them with hugs and went into the kitchen to retrieve a glass of water. Madison followed and stopped me at the refrigerator.

In many ways, Madison St. John was Charlie's protector. She had Charlie's back when he kicked me out of their study group and it was her shoulder that Charlie cried on when he found out that his cousins perished. She said, "Jeremy, Charlie's about to lose it. I don't know if I can hold him together this time. Angela recruited him to ASL."

"Angela was also the admissions counselor assigned to Den and probably half of our whole school."

"Yeah, but because of Angela, Charlie decided to skip on going to Fordham to come here."

"The Fordham University, in New York?"

"Yes."

"Holy shit. He passed up a higher-tiered law school near his home to come to an unaccredited school, here, and still too young to be ranked? He's got balls."

Smiling and nodding, Madison said, "And because of Tom and Tony, he actually loves it here and has never regretted his decision."

"Fuckin' A. And now this. Like they say, 'When you think you got it bad, someone's always got it worse.'"

Madison and I spoke a bit more about how Charlie fell in love with Grundy. Then we walked back to the living room where Lois had just arrived and was hugging Tater.

I tried to ignore it. After all, everyone was hugging everyone that day. I checked on Charlie and Dennis, both of whom were still inconsolable. I tried to comfort them, but both acted like they were coming and going into and out of a vegetative state. As Tater and Lois's prolonged hugging became comforting kisses, I felt myself needing to leave.

I picked up my camera and ran back to the school. I stood on the other side of Slate Creek where I took pictures of what was occurring at ASL. By this time, about an hour had passed since I had spoken to Dennis about what had happened. I was taking pictures for reasons I did not know. I crossed Slate Creek at the main pedestrian bridge, across from ASL's fountain. I crept in for a closer look. There were two hearses waiting in the visitor's parking lot. Everything was quiet but the purring motors of two of death's chariots.

The Grundy townsfolk were gathered around ASL. They were not passive onlookers. In some instances, the townsfolk appeared more upset than the ASL community did. Some shouted things like, "No, please Lord, no!" and "Why is this happening here?"

I walked in the direction of the crime-scene tape, barring anyone from going into the Lion's Lounge. Appearing next to me was Grundy's own, Bluggton Wayne Carr. He grabbed my shoulder and said, "Hey City, they done just took Madeline Short out of hair. I do hope she's okay. She was, or is, my Three L men-tir."

"You're kidding me."

As we walked, I looked at Blugg and counted aloud. I said, "Wait a minute, that's one, Professor Blackwell, two, Dean Sutin, three, Angela Dales, four, Rebecca Brown, five, Stacey Beans, and now there's a sixth?"

Blugg nodded his head as tears dribbled down his bearded face.

"Yep, that's six alright. This place is cursed. I tell ya, this damned place is cursed."

Blugg looked down at the ground, a gesture of respect for many Appalachians, equivalent for looking someone dead in the eye, and continued in his thick country accent, "City, that could have done been us. Or, we might could have stopped 'es shit."

Blugg's "might could have" was the Southwest Virginia way of saying that we should have fucking done something.

As we got closer to the main doors to the Lion's Lounge, sidestepping through the people standing and sobbing, the first gurney slowly made its way out. The body was covered with a white blanket. It was Professor Blackwell, my academic advisor and perhaps the only law school professor in the country to wear bib overalls to his lectures. I knew it was him by the height of the belly.

As the funeral director took Professor Blackwell away from ASL, the sobbing and gentle bustling of sorrow quickened. A bit later, someone pushed a second gurney from the Lion's Lounge. I could tell it was Dean Sutin, ASL's best hope for accreditation, by the trail of people following, weeping. I could not believe he was dead.

The irony of Dean Sutin giving Peter O a break was heartbreaking. In the back of my mind, I was hoping Sutin would give me the same break and allow me to re-start my One L year, if I didn't come out of probation myself. My Plan B possibility died with Dean Sutin. Because of what Peter did with his second chance, I figured ASL would learn its lesson and no longer be lenient. But I knew my loss was nothing compared to the catastrophic loss to Sutin's family and the ASL community.

As Dean Sutin's body left our presence, nothing seemed real. Everything remained quiet. Calm. Somber. After a few more minutes of silence and bewilderment, people started to leave campus. There was nothing left to see. The chaos that Peter O had created remained at ASL only by way of shell casings and drying blood. People left, clinging to each other, borrowing bravery to enable them to walk away and face their sorrow.

I walked back to the Johnson Building with Blugg. As we walked, he said, "I was a-standin' by that Professor Eisen before they brought out 'em bodies. He said ASL wasn't goern' to open back up."

"Seriously?"

"I wouldn't shit my favorite turd."

Fuck.

Now what do I do? What do any of us do? This was one of the only schools 95%

of us could get in to.

When Blugg and I arrived at the Johnson Building, Blugg sat next to Dennis. I entrusted Blugg with the large task of comforting Dennis so I could leave. I quickly packed some of my things and said my good-byes. Blugg and Madison were the only ones who acknowledged that I was leaving.

Madison said, “See you soon?”

“We’ll see.”

Blugg said, “You might want to wait a spell before you come back. The Klan sometimes strikes ’round here when a black kills a white. I ’spect trouble’s a’comin’.”

Madison, who was one of the only other black students in our class, said, “Maybe there’s something to that. Professor Eisen told anyone with color to consider leaving the county until things die down.”

I replied, “Looks like trouble already found its way here.”

And I’m to blame.

# Chapter 14

The guilt. It had been building inside of me even before the shootings. Every time I saw Peter O after I denied his request to take him to Cleveland, he looked angry. He wasn't angry just with me—I could sense that he was angry at the world. When he stopped me in December and said, "I need you to drive me to Cleveland so I can drive taxis and make some money for my family," his body language epitomized desperation. And all I had to do was drive with him for seven hours to possibly help him make it all better. He never said anything about bringing him back.

As if the magnified guilt I carried from denying Peter O a ride to Cleveland wasn't enough, when I left the Johnson Building, I heard the pundits on TV suggest that students like me should have reported warning signs. I surely didn't add warning signs together because I couldn't tell a "warning sign" from some asshole just acting creepy. Nevertheless, my guilt knew no bounds and I blamed myself for not realizing those things could be one in the same.

The main "sign" however, that caused me the most grief, was the one I asked for the previous night. It became apparent that what Dennis told me in the Lion's Lounge wasn't a sign that I'd pass, but was God telling me that I should've gone home. As I drove into West Virginia, a big part of me doubted that I would ever go back to Grundy.

Or maybe it was just fate telling me that it wasn't meant to be.

Once I got to Charleston, I wanted to go the Murphy home, but I remembered Liz hosted book club meetings on Wednesday nights. So I decided to find a bar. I drove through the heart of downtown and peered through the windows of my old college hangouts with hopes I could find a quiet place to sit and digest what occurred that day. Mulligan's was open, one of Charleston's trendier bars. I knew that night to be Working Women's Wednesday, one of Mulligan's promotions that attracted yuppies for Happy Hour. It was always dead after eight, when the drink specials ended.

When I first arrived, I used a phone card to place a call to the Johnson Building in Grundy. Tater answered the phone. I asked how Dennis was holding up.

Tater replied, "Jeremy, you won't believe this. Blugg was right about trouble coming. The KKK is on its way to town and they're going to break into the jail and lynch Peter O."

It sounded so ridiculous. I said, "No way, that's so *To Kill a Mockingbird*. That wouldn't happen now."

"Professor Eisen may have been on to something when he told all of the black students to leave town. I'm from Hazard, Kentucky, and I know a little about the KKK. They're mindless damn idiots, but still around and maybe gettin' fit for a fight."

"Shit. Seriously? I still wouldn't believe Eisen; he's probably inventing all of this to get attention drawn to his egotistical self."

"We're all trying to convince Madison to drive back to Alabama for a while. She says she's not moving. She won't leave Charlie."

"So Charlie is still pretty bad, huh? How's Dennis?"

"Your boy Charlie is all fucked up. Keeps talking about his cousins. He's lying down in your bed. Dennis isn't doing much better. He may even be worse. His parents are driving in as we speak."

I should be there. And now I feel guilty for leaving my friends. Fuck.

After I hung up the phone, I sat down at the bar and ordered a tall, dark beer. I also asked the bartender to put the television closest to me on CNN. After he did, I watched the broadcasters only talking about the ASL shootings in short snippets. Within a matter of just a few hours, the shootings went from top story to only being mentioned briefly in the rolling caption at the bottom of the screen. It didn't take America long to forget. After all, she was getting accustomed to this type of shooting spree.

Around the fourth time I saw the caption, I placed both hands in my hair and took a deep breath. My thoughts were out of control.

And now I feel guilty for not giving Rebecca Brown my belt for a tourniquet. I hope she's okay. Shit.

The bartender asked, "Hey buddy, what's wrong?"

I pointed at the TV and said, "Today's school shooting. It was all my fault. Keep the beers comin'."

I eventually stumbled out of the bar to my jeep. I didn't know whether I was drunk or not because my body and brain didn't feel any different from what they were feeling most of that day. My thoughts were split up into puzzle pieces, mixed up and scattered. Nothing fit together.

When I arrived at the Murphy home, Tim and Liz were already asleep. I crawled into bed in the guest room. I stared at the ceiling for at least an hour. It was spinning.

My life was spinning. I thought about the last time I slept in that bed. It was the previous weekend; the weekend after I discovered ASL placed me on academic probation. Since then, I thought I had turned my life around. I became focused and motivated. On the night of January 16, however, I discovered that my life had spun its way back to West Virginia and to the uncertainty I had about my future. I needed a new day to try to turn my life back around without falling down from all the emotional dizziness. One thing I didn't need a new day for, however, was to receive another sign.

I awoke on January 17, 2002, much as I did the horrible day before. I stood up, took a shower, and wondered where the events of the day would take me. Tim and Liz were getting ready to leave for work. I walked into the kitchen and gave Liz a kiss on the cheek.

Somberly, I said, "Good morning, Murphys."

Liz smiled warmly. She said, "Good morning, Jeremy. Chairman Wooton told Tim about what happened in Grundy at yesterday's afternoon committee meeting. How are you doing?"

"I still don't know. In some sort of weird shock, I think. It really hasn't hit me too much yet. Don't know if I'll ever go back."

I placed a few slices of bread into the toaster and continued, "I think fate is telling me that I never should've gone back to begin with."

Tim smirked his here-we-go-again smirk and said, "Well, if you don't go back, you'll be quitting—twice in a few days. Never seen that done before."

Despite living in West Virginia for over twenty years, Tim still had some of his homegrown Connecticut accent. With it, he continued, "Maybe you need to spend some time in the family room with Willie Mays. You know, he made that over-the-shoulder catch on his own. He didn't quit on it and he ran the ball down with hard work."

Tim was referring to "The Catch," a large photo of which he had framed and placed above his mantle. It was an unbelievable grab that Willie Mays made in the 1954 World Series that set the tone for Tim's childhood hero New York Giants sweeping my heavily favored Cleveland Indians.

"Yeah, but Tim, that catch was unbelievable. With all that segregation stuff going on back then, it was his destiny to catch it."

Tim smiled and shook his head as he closed his briefcase. Liz, who began buttering my toast, kept her focus on the buttering when she said, "Jeremy, do you maybe think maybe you're not talking about fate, but something else?"

The Murphys were Catholic, but like many Catholics, they didn't advertise it. They went to Mass on Sundays, put money into the collection basket, and sent their kids to Catholic school. But they didn't talk a whole lot about religion. But I could sense that's where Liz was going, despite her not saying it. My mom, on the other hand, had been on my ass about not praying for years. If my mom were in the room at that moment, she would have no doubt quickly followed up to what Liz had said.

I replied, "Well, Liz. You could be right. Maybe the Good Lord has a plan for me. But ASL placing me on probation and then a few days later, these murders—it has to be destiny sending me a message, not divine intervention."

"Yeah, but Jeremy, do you think maybe those two things could be one in the same?"

⚖

After the Murphys went to work, I sat around their house and did my best to quash any temptations to quit law school—again. I kept telling myself that Dean Sutin would have wanted better from me and that I owed it to Professor Blackwell to keep trying. Hanging out with my old friends at the capitol would hopefully motivate me.

It was the beginning of the 2002 West Virginia sixty-day legislative session and things around the statehouse were lively. Lobbyists were bouncing from office to office, looking for the inside scoop and school kids were everywhere, learning about the legislative process. As I entered the staff area for the judiciary committee, I accidentally bumped into Senator Kulick.

"Oh, are you back?" he said. "We heard what happened. They're probably closing the school, huh? Are you coming back to your old job?"

Although Senator Kulick knew I was a friend of leadership and it would be a bad idea to treat me like shit, I sensed he was fucking with me. Once a prick, always a prick.

"I don't know, Senator. If you will excuse me, I'm looking for Tim."

"He's right over there by the coffee machine. Please bring me some if you wouldn't mind."

Without the energy to fire back, but with no intent on following through, I simply said, "Sure, Senator."

Chairman Wooton spotted me from the other end of the hall. Like I still worked there, he said, "Jeremy, I'm glad you're here. We've been having some trouble with some of the microphones. The audio guys said you'd know how to fix it."

"Yeah, sure. I'm not doing anything today."

As if he just received an epiphany, Chairman Wooton stopped, turned back towards me, and said, "Oh, and I'm sorry to hear about what happened at your school yesterday. I also heard that your grades weren't that great. I'm sure you'll pick them up. You're too bright not to."

"Thanks, Mister Chairman. I'll get to work on those mikes for you right away."

I believed going back to work, if only for a bit, would do me a lot of good. As I began working on Chairman Wooton's sound issue, I deflated. Something that used to take me ten minutes was going to take me much longer. It was like most departments of my brain were out to lunch. I couldn't help thinking that even if Chairman Wooton let me come back and I had to again deal with Senator Kulick, perhaps it wouldn't be that bad.

Everyone will understand.

Coming back to work for senate judiciary would beat going back to Grundy this semester.

I'd rather put up with Kulick's shit then to have to find a way to study after this.

After about an hour, and upon fixing Chairman Wooton's audio problem, Tim found me and told me the Senate was considering a bill I researched, drafted, and presented for the judiciary committee before I left.

He said, "This could be reason for you to celebrate later. And it just so happens that the big coal reception is tonight."

"I won't feel like celebrating, but if my bill passes, maybe that'll keep me from being too much of a downer."

After I spoke with Tim, I walked down by the Kanawha River, hoping the calm current of the water would allow me to clear my head. As I opened the heavy brass capitol doors and headed towards the river, I walked up to the large statue of Abraham Lincoln that greeted visitors to the statehouse.

Just as Americans consider George Washington the father of the United States, West Virginians revere Abraham Lincoln as West Virginia's founder. Lincoln created West Virginia by signing Proclamation 100, the document freeing the northern-most southern state from its Confederate host. The features of the Lincoln statue are a perfect representation of different emotions colliding into one portrayal. All within one look, Lincoln's facial feature can be interpreted as a look of grief, a look of hope, a look of determination, or a look of sorrow. Lincoln's humble figure faces the Kanawha River, looking to the ground. Or, as I felt standing under him at that particular moment, looking directly at me.

As I gazed up at Lincoln's mysterious eyes, cast in a solid weathered bronze, I felt them trying to tell me something. I felt like Abraham Lincoln was sending me a message.

"Well? I'm listening. Just don't send me a sign, okay?"

# Chapter 15

"With Penelope firin' on all cylinders, I reckon I've been busier than a cat coverin' shit on a marble floor. But more importantly, how are you, son?"

It was the first time I had spoken to Hammer Mike since the shootings. I called him from the Murphy rotary phone while I waited for them to get off work before the coal reception.

"I guess I'm okay. Mom told you about what happened?"

"Yep. I would've called you but no one knows how to ever get a hold of you. Son, like I always say, get a fuckin' cell phone like the rest of the world."

"Yeah, yeah. I just feel like I could've stopped the whole thing, you know? It's killing me. Maybe something is pulling me back home?"

I heard my dad light a cigarette as he said, "Fuck that. You're not shot, are you? If you're not physically injured, you're going to sack up and finish school—or get kicked out tryin'. If you attempt to come back home beforehand, I'll make you shit something you never ate. Just so we're clear, okay?"

"I got you. But the shooter wanted me to drive him to Cleveland in December. Dad, this is all my fault."

Hammer Mike replied, "What the fuck makes you think he wasn't coming here to pick up bombs or machine guns or some shit? Son, don't flatter yourself thinking you could have somehow changed what that crazy mutherfucker did."

"Dude, I saw it in his eyes. He wasn't hell-bent on murder then. He just wanted to be a man and restore some honor to his family."

As I imagined him punching my arm with a powerful right, Hammer Mike said, "Suuuuuure. Bub, every path has puddles. It ain't about honor. Did I go ape-shit and kill people when your mom kicked me out of the house for the final time? I lost my honor, but..."

"No."

"It took some time, but I got my shit together. The Nigerian mutherfucker should've gotten his shit together, but he didn't. That's the simple fact of what happened. If you're feeling guilty, do something about it and get your shit together."

⚖

In the hopping, festive political soiree known as the big coal reception, Tim updated me on the status of my cyberstalking bill. It was a new draft, within the same spirit of the one that I authored—making it a misdemeanor to stalk someone in West Virginia via computer means. It passed the Senate that day. Tim said the House would likely complicate it, but he thought it would also pass there and the governor would soon sign it.

I regularly attended each lobbyist's reception when I proudly worked for the Burnside family's ancestral home state. The receptions were always extravagant and fun. The reception of January 17, 2002, was no different, except that I didn't have plans to get drunk to the point where I'd hit on cute interns or tell the legislators how to vote. The most mischief I thought about partaking in was requesting Hansen's Mmmbop for Senator Kulick to sing as a high-end karaoke business served up the entertainment.

The karaoke didn't begin until well into the night. The karaoke business had a trunk with costumes in it to try to make the singers more amusing. I thought that West Virginia's finest politicians trying to sing pop hits was amusement enough.

Tim Murphy volunteered for the Kulick Mmmbop request mission, or at least he said he would handle it if I fetched him a beer. But the joke was on me. When the karaoke lady called my name for the next song, I approached the stage and utilized what was in the trunk to hide who I was, hoping Tim did not select the popular Hansen tune for me.

That night, I didn't want to be the depressing Jeremy Burnside. I wanted to be someone fun. I didn't want people to look at me and say, "Hey, that's the guy from that Appalachian school shooting!" I wanted to pretend the murders never happened so I didn't care to belt out the lyrics to Mmmbop if it made me feel a little better.

I quickly chugged a beer to help me loosen up for the unexpected. The karaoke lady then stopped the song she was singing and made an announcement.

"Ladies and gentlemen, the governor of the great State of West Virginia, Bob Wise!"

That certainly was unexpected. The governor, like Chairman Wooton, rarely made appearances at the lobbyist schmooze-fests. A loud cheer came over the reception crowd, which had probably exceeded 300 people. When the clapping stopped, the karaoke lady continued, "And to welcome Mister and Mrs. Wise to the dance floor, Jeremy Burnside!"

Oh, shit.

I initially felt like I wanted to teleport to Mulligan's. In addition to being nervous about singing in front of the governor, I was paranoid that the whole crowd remembered my name from the cover of that day's paper where an Associated Press reporter called me before I left Grundy and quoted me as saying that Peter O "was a little bit not there." But I didn't have long to feel uncomfortable. West Virginia's top government official, who was also a former U.S. Congressman, wanted to shake the dirt off his feet.

As I stepped to the middle of the stage, the karaoke lady searched for the song Tim picked out for me. I then started pacing in my large pink boa, 16th century jester's hat, and large floppy overcoat. As the crowd fell silent, I stopped moving and stood there. On the stage, alone.

They're all looking at me.

Are they disgusted that I'm here having fun and not grieving in Grundy?

Ten seconds of the karaoke lady searching her song database became thirty seconds. I had the microphone. I felt like everyone was waiting for me to say something. I felt like I was in a bad dream and with everyone surely wondering if I had lost it.

The karaoke lady finally found what she was looking for and leaned into my microphone. She announced, "Everyone get on the floor and dance with the governor! It'll be a gas, gas, gas!"

Despite the pressures of being in front of most of the legislature, anyone and everyone important in West Virginia politics, including the governor, I lifted my head up to the sky and blocked out Grundy, Virginia, as much as heaven would let me. I screamed into the microphone.

"Hell-OOOO Charleston!"

The crowd clapped and whistled.

"Are we having a good time to-night?"

The distinguished gathering cheered again.

"Are you ready to shake your asses with me?"

I caught a peek at the governor smiling. He was ready to boogie. Not that I wasn't already nervous, but Governor Wise was an expert dancer. Well, not a dancer, a clogger. West Virginia's head honcho was a master of this form of mountain dancing. When I saw the song title pop up on the screen, I felt so relieved knowing that it wasn't what I thought it would be. I was about to sing the Rolling Stones' *Jumpin' Jack Flash* for Cloggin' Bob Wise.

I started my Mick Jagger chicken strut across the stage at about the same point the Rolling Stones' classic began its famous opening riff, courtesy of Tim Murphy. I had already made a complete fool of myself.

Ahh, fuck it. If they want a good time, I'll give it to them. I don't give a shit at this point.

While strutting and dancing, I shouted, "I was BORN in a..." As the song continued, everyone was dancing, including Governor Wise, who busted in at points into some of his famed mountain dance. The karaoke lady just stood aside and laughed as I danced and strutted all over the stage and performed a brief jig down on the dance floor during Keith Richards's swanky, upbeat solo.

When the song was over, and after several high fives, I went straight to the bathroom. I opened up a vacant stall and went in. I thought about what I had just done and cried.

I have to get back to Grundy.

There's no way I can ever move back here.

⚖

An older woman with bright white hair whom I had never met before was standing near the door for the ladies room. She was wearing an expensive silver gown and glowing jewelry. She was in her early sixties, but with her busting cleavage and gown slit to her tanned tone thigh, some my age would say she was hot. The silver fox lit a Virginia Slim and walked towards me as I left the men's room.

"So you're Jeremy Burnside," she said in an alluring voice, "I read your quote today and have been closely following what happened at your school."

"Yes, pardon me, Ma'am, but I gotta' go. Not in the mood to talk about that."

I began to walk away. The insistent woman grabbed my hand. She was also wearing narrow glasses that she lowered in order to look me in the eyes. She said, "You can't blame yourself for the shooting. Blame the gun."

"Huh? The gun? But my classmate pulled the trigger."

The risqué woman smiled, like she knew I would say that. She said, "Ask yourself if the man that did the killing could've done so without the gun."

I defensively said, "Well, he has rights..."

I stopped and paused. I looked to the ground.

But so did the people who were killed.

Peter O's wimpy ass couldn't have killed without a gun. This lady has a point.

I looked back up. The woman was gone and I spent the remainder of that night looking for her. She may have only existed in my muddled-up mind. For the rest of that evening, I came to some serious revelations.

Guns kill.

America allows people to buy guns just as easily as buying a bag of chips.

We can't jaywalk, but we can buy assault weapons?

Now that I think about it, the gun that Peter O fired shares the blame for this.

# Chapter 16

On my way back to Grundy, I thought about the brief exchange I had with the woman in the silver gown regarding the goddamn gun: the equalizer that the cowardly Peter O needed to inflict his frustration upon the world. Contrary to some of the crap being argued in the media in the few days after the shootings, he couldn't have found another way to inflict great harm to six people in a matter of minutes—he was weak.

Peter O had one of those handshakes that felt slimy in your palm. He didn't have much fat, but didn't have much muscle mass either. It was like his body was made up of some weird substance resembling that of compost. Peter O was soft—and he stunk. Perhaps he thought his mouth and mind games could make up for his missing man features. When those things stopped working, he brought a gun to town, like a little wimpy cowboy exacting revenge on helpless, unarmed Indians.

Another pro-gun proliferation argument was that even if guns were illegal, Peter O would have found one, somehow. These pundits argued this, but failed to establish where a guy like Peter O, in Grundy, Virginia, would find such a violent treasure. It's not like there was a Buchanan County Mafia that Peter O could have sold his soul to in exchange for a gun. Even if there were one, I would think that such a fictional crime organization would be racist enough to prevent one of Grundy's only black men from obtaining some firepower.

There was another argument—if Peter O wasn't legally able to purchase a gun, he would have traveled to a big city where guns are allegedly sold everywhere. That argument hit close to home with me as I prevented him from traveling to a big city to buy his weapon on the mean streets, like Hammer Mike's Marijuana Alley. Even if Peter O did find his way up there, I'm pretty sure that Cleveland's Bloods and its local Folk gang would have laughed at him. The Crips would have kicked his ass.

As the lady in the silver gown suggested, if it wasn't so easy for Peter O to get a legal firearm, he wouldn't have found an equalizer—and he wouldn't have found other ways to kill. I knew him, the NRA bigmouths did not. After analyzing each pro-stupid, pro-gun argument in my mind on that drive back to Grundy, it became obvious to me that something had to be done about guns.

School shootings were inevitably going to rise and Peter O's rampage would likely get out-done year after year by more lost souls committed to murder. Every time I heard the word Columbine, I thought of a school shooting and death—then governmental inaction. I foresaw people hearing the words Appalachian School of Law and immediately thinking of another school shooting. Those people would think about bullets tearing through the flesh of otherwise healthy students and teachers. Those people would think about guns, but would learn nothing from the ASL shootings, just as the world learned nothing from the Columbine shootings.

An event such as Columbine should've been a sociological modifier. But our leaders did nothing. Someone had to do something, though. On my drive back to Grundy, I decided that I would be that someone.

That's how I'll make this guilt go away.

⚖

As I drove through downtown Grundy, I felt the mourning atmosphere of January 16. It was as if I was entering the Twilight Zone, which the show identified as the "middle ground between light and shadow." Near the only downtown traffic light was a mural of the high school mascot, a golden wave guy with eyes and arms and to which I called "Urine Man!" He used to look like he was getting ready to fight. But that day, it looked like he was trying to run out of town. People walking the street looked mindless. Slate Creek looked like it was flowing in the opposite direction.

Before I entered the Johnson Building, I became anxious and began asking questions:

Are the three survivors going to pull through?

Did the KKK lynch Peter O?

Who's going to teach Contracts? Who'll be our Dean?

I arrived at the Johnson Building that Friday, January 18 evening at around 9:00 P.M. My room had been taken over by Dennis's parents. As soon as they saw me, each gave me a hug. Dennis's mother looked at me as if I was a soldier who just got back from war.

She said, "Jeremy, we were all so worried about you. We hope you don't mind us staying in your room."

I had never met Dennis's parents, but was glad they were there. Their presence certainly added comfort where comfort was due.

"I'm fine. You all can have it. I've passed out, I mean, slept on the couch a lot last semester. How are my roommates?"

Dennis's father looked at me and shook his head. He said, "Well, Jeremy, our Dennis is taking this really hard. He's with that fella Tater right now, over at the community center. ASL set up counselors for you all over there."

I said, "He feels really guilty. Dennis witnessed a lot. He's going to be okay, right?"

Dennis's mother hugged her husband and walked closer to me with tears running down her eyes. She said, "My Denny blames himself for this. He's beating himself up over constantly joking that Peter would bring a gun to ASL and go postal, as he calls it. He thinks his jokes somehow got back to Peter and gave him the idea to actually do it."

"Ma'am, I know he probably thinks that, but I'm sorry, that's foolish."

Dennis's mother reached in and gave me another hug. Softly into my ear she said, "But I try to tell him that the devil got into Peter O and Peter couldn't fight him off."

After I spoke with Dennis's parents for a bit about the duties Dennis and I had when we worked for the West Virginia legislature, I heard Dennis walking up the stairs with Tater. When I saw Dennis's face, I noticed that his eyes were bloodshot and his face was grim.

Tater said, "Hey Jeremy, how're you doin'?"

"I'm good. Sorry I just up and left but I needed to get the hell out of here. How are things at school?"

Dennis looked like he was fighting another breakdown. I placed my arm on his shoulder and said to him, "Dude, you can't blame yourself for this. I think Peter O got the gun shortly after I told him to fuck off when he asked me to give him a ride to Cleveland. I keep thinking that his plea was a cry for help to get him away from Grundy before he did something rash."

Dennis mustered up enough strength to say, "Thanks, Jeremy. I just wish I had never made those jokes, that's all."

Soon after everyone went to bed, I fell right to sleep. I had a disturbing dream. I dreamt that I was on the top floor of the library and was helping people escape through the windows onto an overhang. Once I did that, no one had anywhere to go. I had trapped them and Peter O was making his way towards us. I tried to distract him by throwing a book across the room. He didn't see or hear it. I charged him. He pointed his gun at me.

I woke up.

While I wiped the sweat off my forehead and realized it was just a dream, I heard a noise coming from the kitchen.

"Come and get it!"

It was morning, January 19, 2002, and Dennis's parents had a big breakfast cooking. As I attempted to awaken, Dennis's mom gyrated a plate of biscuits under my nose to provoke me to get up.

We all ate breakfast together, and Dennis seemed to be doing a lot better. We spoke about what we were hearing in the papers and on the news. Someone brought up a possible lawsuit.

"Based on what?" I asked.

Tater said, "Jeremy, if we all knew Peter O was crazy, the school should have, too."

"So? The people who knew most about Peter O's state of mind were Sutin, as he seemed to always coddle him, and Blackwell, who I saw give Peter a ride the night before."

"We go to a school filled with future lawyers," Tater said after taking a swig of orange juice, "Many of whom have lawyer parents and friends. Someone will be filing a lawsuit."

I said, "What I think should happen is that..."

Dennis's dad, who was the polar opposite of Dennis and a staunch Republican, must have believed he and I were in harmony and attempted to finish my thought with, "... allow more law abiding citizens to carry guns. The proof of how effective they can be is in how the killings here stopped."

I couldn't resist myself and said, "I was standing right there. I would like to know how you think the murders stopped."

Dennis's mom said, "Okay, boys, now's not the time."

"Those fellas putting a gun on the colored guy. It's all over my gun club website. The guns saved who-knows-how-many."

Don't say anything.

Be cool.

"I gotta get some air. Thanks for breakfast."

My head was steaming and I was about to explode. I wanted to tell Dennis's dad that he didn't fucking know what he was talking about and that he was shitting out the mouth like a damn fool. I wanted to explain how Peter O had already given up, more or less, before he was tackled and taken to the ground. Those guns being on him had nothing to do with his surrender.

CNN and other news broadcasts held debates on that same topic. I was getting the feeling the murders at ASL were being glamorized, with guns being hailed as heroic violence stoppers. With trumpets blaring, women swooning, and parading arms-bearing titans covered by the light of God, the media touted the same species of weapon responsible for three dead and three wounded in Grundy. Imagine that shit. Ridiculous.

The man was out of fucking bullets.

Once I left the Johnson Building, I had to see the aftermath for myself, so I began my walk towards the school. The brisk January air felt so lonely, as if I was the only one breathing it. On Main Street, I didn't see any cars moving, people walking, or the occasional stray dog crossing the street. The town was dead. The media vans that were left over in ASL's parking lots were Grundy's only sign of life.

As I crossed Slate Creek on the pedestrian bridge that led to ASL's fountain and main gate, I noticed a sea of flowers atop and surrounding the ASL marble sign. There were additional bouquets on the steps to the main entrance. As I approached the wrought iron gate, I could smell the haunting scent of death's aftermath: the strong odor of potent cleaning materials. After I entered the Lion's Lounge and inspected the areas on the floor where the wounded had lain, I stood and looked around.

Jesus Christ.

ASL looked like it had been quarantined and abandoned. The emotional impact of the shootings had not completely hit me and I remained numb, angry. I looked left to the wooden lions I once thought to be my totems. They no longer stood so proud. I looked to my right and there was a notice posted, hung on the wall by a single piece of clear tape. It was a list of the students who made the Dean's List for the fall semester. I stared at the paper for a while.

My name has to be on the same list for the spring semester, or I'm doomed.

Momentarily motivated after looking at the list, I decided that I needed to try to move on. While Dennis, his parents and Tater visited the nearby interstate park, I took that opportunity to move out of the Johnson Building and into my new apartment above the local beauty school. I stayed up late sorting my things. Anything that had to do with fun or distraction, such as video games, stayed in a box.

The next day I attended the memorial service for Dean L. Anthony Sutin. I put on a dress shirt and tie and drove to Grundy High School, a long baseball toss from the YMCA. Several of Dean Sutin's closest friends and relatives were there, most of whom had traveled from civilization. I gave his family a lot of credit for having his memorial service in Grundy. After all, Dean Sutin was from Bayshore, New York, graduated Harvard Law, and had previously worked in Washington D.C. Of all of these places, Grundy proved to be most important to him.

And judging by the large out-of-state turnout, Dean Sutin's loved ones must have appreciated his devotion to ASL and Buchanan County. Judging by the multitude of townsfolk in attendance, Grundy did as well. As I sat through the service, I wished I would have had a chance to have gotten to know the man, other than from his orientation speech about who would fail out and his probation memorandum advising me that I was close to being one of them.

As several speakers spoke about Dean Sutin's life, I worried that his vision would fade and that ASL would perish. I also thought about Professor Blackwell and Angela

Dales and the vision they had for ASL and Buchanan County. All three victims shared the same dream of bringing a high level of education to a rural, depressed area. They had hopes that residents of rustic Appalachia would no longer settle for working in the failing coalmines or depend on welfare, but would strive for the moon. Dean Sutin brought and cultivated the idea, Professor Blackwell promoted it throughout the community and in his classrooms, and Angela Dales lived it.

Peter O and his fucking gun killed it. It was time for me to get to work.

# Chapter 17

It was November 1862, and the morale of the country was in desperate need of a Union victory during the Civil War. President Abraham Lincoln tried to be patient with General George B. McClellan, who was beloved by his soldiers. But McClellan was hesitant to attack Virginia and press the Confederate army, led by Robert E. Lee. After extended periods of inaction, Lincoln fired McClellan and sought out the guy he wanted all along to lead his troops.

President Lincoln had one man in mind: Major General Ambrose E. Burnside. Lincoln's reverence for Burnside led to an unwavering confidence in Burnside's abilities. In the late fall of 1862, Lincoln attempted to persuade Burnside to accept the ultimate role, but Burnside did not want the job. Admittedly, Burnside felt that he was not competent enough to lead all Union forces against what surprisingly became a formidable Army of Northern Virginia, a force filled with spirited, underestimated rebels. He also didn't want to feel guilty for the military demotion of his friend, General McClellan.

Finally, on November 9, 1862, however, General Burnside accepted Lincoln's charge and became leader of the entire Army of the Potomac. General Burnside answered his calling and marched on Virginia.

# Chapter 18

In my second night in my new apartment, I thought about some things I could do to make the guilt go away so I could concentrate on my studies. It didn't take long for me to remember that eerie feeling I had when I looked up at the Abraham Lincoln statue at the West Virginia statehouse. There was something about the way I felt at that moment that made me believe that not only did I want to do something, but that I was being called to do something bold about the proliferation of guns.

President Lincoln enlisted my services and I was just waiting for orders. Like General Burnside, I had doubts in myself. I didn't know that I could win the hearts of my classmates. But, like General Burnside, who probably also doubted whether he could win his soldiers' hearts from his friend, I felt an overwhelming inner duty to try.

When I awoke on Monday, January 21, our last day off before ASL scheduled us to return to class, I received a group email indicating that Stacey Beans, Rebecca Brown, and Madeline Short were all going to be okay. There was also a message from Dean Lund confirming that we would have a normal class schedule beginning the next day, and that Doctor McGhee would be Professor Blackwell's replacement in Contracts II. Normally, I would have trembled at the thought of Doctor McGhee, with her intimidating cane and mastery of the Socratic Method, teaching Contracts II. But my mind was on the shootings and doing something about the murders.

I became certain that Abraham Lincoln commissioned me to march on Virginia, so I was going to march. I thought my message had to shock people into thinking about life's big picture outside of Grundy's small boundaries. I'd paint it for them: it shouldn't be so damn easy for a violent lunatic like Peter O to buy a gun.

That day was Martin Luther King Day. While using the internet to research my newfound gun control position, I clicked on a link about Dr. King. The website discussed various marches and causes he orchestrated. It appeared that Dr. King never laid down for anything, that he took a fight as far as he could take it. As I read more and more about him, I became enlightened about the hope he instilled in so many people. Dr. King demanded a change that many thought would never come.

If America can change its legal perception on blacks, why can't it change its legal perception on guns?

Perhaps it's because the weak gun control movement doesn't have a Dr. King.

Peace fighters need a champion.

It's not that I ever thought I could make an immeasurable impact like Dr. King, but I did feel I could make some change. Soon after the Civil War, General Burnside became the very first president of the National Rifle Association, an organization he helped start. Surely, I felt, that tidbit of information would help me get attention from the media so I could discuss how its founding president would have been appalled by what the NRA had become.

Civil War generals, like General Burnside, organized the NRA because they hated seeing poor shooting from their soldiers. These veterans founded the NRA to promote better shooting skills, not to fight for a wild-west America where everyone is packing heat. In the 1930s, the NRA actually supported gun control. It wasn't until the 1960s, however, that it changed its tune to the shrouded anthems of violence it rallies behind today.

I had no problem with self-defense, hunting, shooting sports, or armed law enforcement. Those things were good things. But I had a hard time justifying why "law abiding citizens," as the NRA put it, needed automatic weapons with an unlimited supply of ammunition to protect their Second Amendment "rights."

Before I started my research, I just assumed that the Second Amendment afforded everyone the right to carry guns. After I finished my research, however, I wondered how the hell the NRA, or any other gun group, could say that the right to bear arms applied to individuals. The amendment applies to "well-regulated" citizen militias only. Nothing in it suggests that individuals have the right to use a bazooka to hunt squirrel. The amendment was meant to protect citizens against a tyrannical government. General Burnside certainly would have agreed with this rationale, and he wasn't even a lawyer.

In the 1920s and 1930s when the NRA was a strong backer of gun control, one of Burnside's early NRA presidential descendants, Karl T. Frederick, didn't stress that the Second Amendment had much consequence to the NRA or an individual's alleged right to bear arms. Frederick was a Harvard-educated lawyer. He was also a 1920 Olympic gold medal pistol winner and likely shared Burnside's views about advancing shooting sports, not the extreme proliferation of guns throughout society.

In a 1934 Congressional committee meeting to discuss pending gun control legislation, Frederick said, "I have never believed in the general practice of carrying weapons. I seldom carry one . . . do not believe in the general promiscuous toting of guns. I think it should be sharply restricted and only under licenses." Sounds like "well-regulated" to me.

Karl Frederick, who lived in a time of real mobsters, violence, and extreme desperation caused by the Great Depression, did not advance the current NRA position that more guns were needed to curb more gun violence. In fact, an argument could be made that when he said, "sharply restricted," he meant that we should have restrictions in place like they have in Japan: no handguns and a very restrictive process involving training and psychological testing to be able to purchase low-caliber rifles.

And as an educated lawyer, Frederick most certainly did not depend upon a very liberal reading of the Second Amendment to advance his organization into political dominance. It would take a wacky Supreme Court decision declaring that we are all in a state militia to verify the modern NRA's idiotic interpretations. To me, though, the Second Amendment still meant that an individual had a right to bear arms in a well-regulated militia against an overly oppressive government, not against other individuals.

Did that make me a nut?

Did that make Karl Frederick a nut?

Did my views to promote measures preventing nutjobs from obtaining firepower make me a left-wing radical?

I didn't give a shit.

⚖

Virginia did not require background checks of all sales of guns at gun shows. Although word was circulating around campus that Peter O probably did not get his gun from a gun show, I hoped that the law would soon change to prevent people with violent or psychological issues from buying a gun without a background check—a premise Karl Frederick would have undoubtedly supported.

My research led me to a good explanation by the Americans for Gun Safety Foundation, which described the gun-show loophole as having a double standard for gun purchases: gun stores required background checks, but sales at gun shows by unlicensed sellers did not. Upon the conclusion of my research, I drafted a bill with language that, if enacted into law, would eliminate this dual standard for gun purchases in gun-loving Virginia. Somehow, I was going to get it passed. Somehow, I was going to start a revolution. Then surely the guilt I carried from the shootings would dissipate.

When I awoke for class that Tuesday, I didn't care anything about my vision quest, what my classmates had been doing since the shootings, or anything else but getting my drafted legislation in the hands of a politician to show the world that ASL was not always going to be known for January 16. Similar to Dr. King, I had a dream. My dream was that ASL would be known for fighting the proliferation of guns.

Our first class after the tragedy was Criminal Law. Dean Lund took over that day to discuss how ASL was planning to move forward. His voice was somber when I thought it should have been strong, ready to fight. My classmates were crying. This wasn't the same school they attended just days before. Some of our classmates were dead or still in the hospital. Our tiny Appalachian school had since hired security guards.

Isn't anyone ready to fight?

I can't listen to this shit.

Gallantry. Action. Protest. I wanted it all. A collective rise against the NRA's falsely engrained and disturbingly absurd ideal that everyone, and I mean everyone, in the United States should be permitted to carry a gun. My blood was boiling. I didn't want to grieve. Hell no, I wanted to march!

Realizing that that particular moment wasn't right for a rousing speech, I decided to cool off and wait until I thought it through. I wanted to do something great, but I needed wise advice. So after class, I spoke to Mrs. Frehley.

Everyone knew Mrs. Frehley was having a hard time with the shootings, especially since she thought Peter O was after her. I was going to use her feelings to my advantage, or should I say, to the advantage of my movement about peace. I went to Mrs. Frehley's office, told her of my idea, and handed her the piece of legislation I had drafted.

Mrs. Frehley skimmed it over, smiled, and said, "As you can imagine, Jeremy, this past week has been very difficult for me. I also think something should be done about guns, but I don't know if people will listen."

"Well, I want ASL to be the voice of reason. I want to get a group of people together to ride to Richmond and solicit the introduction of this bill, or something similar, to the legislature."

Mrs. Frehley chuckled. She said, "Gosh, Jeremy, to think I thought you were crazy for coming back to ASL when I discovered your fall semester grades!"

I didn't chuckle back.

"I'm dead serious. I'm going to do this."

Mrs. Frehley sat back in her spring-loaded wooden office chair. She knew I was serious, but didn't know whether to get involved. She just sat and stared at the document.

I said, "Well? What do you think? What should I do?"

"Jeremy, I can see that you're serious. You are most certainly ambitious. I just don't know if I can—or should—get involved. Tell you what, get a few more faculty members on board and I'll talk to the administration about it."

When Mrs. Frehley told me she would talk to the administration about my plans, I got excited. Upon leaving her office, I walked briskly down the hall, to the other wing of the school. I walked up to Professor Blackwell's closed door and debated my next move, just as I did when I sought him out for advice on coming back to Grundy. This time, the cheery bearded man who enjoyed teaching in his overalls wasn't counseling someone on the other side.

Then I did it again. For some reason, I went to the last place on earth I thought I would ever go again. I was desperate for support and impatient to search elsewhere. Once more, I went to see Dickey Eisen and unfortunately, his door was again open.

I stepped inside of his office and hesitantly asked, “Professor Eisen, do you have a few minutes?”

Upon seeing me, Dickey shook his head in disbelief.

“You. I don’t really have time, but I do have a feeling you’re going to tell me something interesting. Go ahead.”

“I’m here because I have an idea about how ASL can show the world that it isn’t going to be known solely for the January 16$^{th}$ tragedy.”

I sat down and didn’t care if he minded. Dickey smiled and sat up.

“Oh?”

I said, “I heard that you used to draft legislation for the Illinois legislature.”

Dickey then leaned back in his chair with arrogance. “Yes, I was responsible for drafting some of the most dynamic legislation in the country. Many states used me and my wisdom to develop their own carbon-copy laws.”

“But that’s why I’m…”

With Dickey’s face looking like he was basking in his own fart, he interrupted me, “So go on and amuse me, please, Mister Burnside. Continue.”

Dickey’s attitude didn’t faze me. I was driven and on a mission.

“Well, I’ve got this bill I drafted on gun control here that I want to get introduced in Virginia’s legislature. Mrs. Frehley said she’d help me if I found more faculty support and State Senator Leslie Byrne looks to be a great ally. Senator Byrne already suggested that because of what happened here, we need more gun control.”

Dickey snickered and shook his head. He sarcastically said, “Sure. I’ll take a look at your bill. Just set it right here. I’ll get right on it.”

Dickey patted the corner of his desk while donning a smirk.

I called Dickey out on his disingenuous tone. I said, “Are you being serious? Because it seems you’re laughing at me. If you think this is a joke, I need to take this somewhere else.”

Dickey stopped snickering and said, “No, you can leave it with me. I do have a lot of things to do today though before I can read your, um, bill, is it?"

I reluctantly left the bill on Dickey's desk and got up to leave his office. I stopped and said, "Oh, one more thing, can I have a few minutes before your lecture tomorrow to present my idea to the class?"

Dickey slapped his desk, rose up, and said, "You want to do what? Don't you know where we are? People treat their guns better than their own mothers around here."

I set my backpack down.

"Are you happy with the way people look at ASL? Do you give a shit? Someone from your class comes in here and wants to do something positive and you laugh? I'm taking this back. And I'm going to report to Mrs. Frehley that you laughed at the same idea she said she'd support."

I picked up the bill off his desk, shouldered my backpack, and headed to the door.

"Wait. Wait. Come back in here."

I stopped. Word around campus was that Dickey wanted ASL to grant him tenure. I assumed he needed all the faculty support he could get, including that of my supporter, Mrs. Frehley.

Dickey sighed then continued, "Okay, you can have two minutes at the beginning of tomorrow's class and I'll look at your bill. I was only smiling because I think you may have lost your mind."

I slid my draft legislation towards him on his clean and empty desk and said, "Here's the bill, see you tomorrow in class. And by the way, the only way someone will make a difference about guns is if they lose their mind. If you say I've lost mine, then I must be on the right track."

When I walked out of Dickey's office, I knew I had made a big mistake. What have I done? He'll try to sabotage me.

But, if he gives me the time, I know I can win everyone over. Just like in September.

# Chapter 19

Doctor Patricia "Patti" McGhee was my fall semester Torts professor and one nasty bitch. She drove a dark red Jaguar, the color of Lucifer. During our first class, Doctor McGhee promised us that she was going to "prune the insignificance out of our class," even if it meant failing everyone. She didn't believe in the bell curve and fought hard with the administration to keep her failure rate high.

With Doctor McGhee controlling our only four-credit grade in Torts, the chances for even ASL's elite to transfer were bad. And within the first few weeks of fall semester classes, the awkward stage of a One L life, I became a collateral victim to Doctor McGhee's vicious attack on one of our best.

Doctor McGhee was about sixty years old, with a fading Irish accent and a soft, demeaning voice. When she spoke to us, it was like she was releasing red ants all over our bodies to gnaw away at any hope of a right answer. Adding to Doctor McGhee's malevolent nature, she had a limp that many of us suspected she got after kicking a student in the head for not reading. To compensate for this ailment, she carried a mahogany wood cane with a small sculpture of the goddess Athena at the top that she clutched as she walked.

During every Torts class, Doctor McGhee owned not only our signature on the attendance sheet, but our souls. She was a true advocate of the Socratic Method and if she randomly called on you and you were not prepared, she swallowed you and spit you out as a spiritless failure. Even if you had the book's right answer, it was not always *her* right answer. Doctor McGhee didn't discriminate when tearing apart a response; she hated everyone the same. Except for "intellectually infantile lectern trolls." She did hate them more than anyone.

Lectern trolls are overzealous students who frequently hurry towards the lectern immediately after class. These trolls always claim that they had a valid question for the professor about the class discussion or the reading assignment. It is obvious, however, that the trolls approach the lectern to suck up. Portia Simmons was the queen of lectern trolls—which is why Doctor McGhee tried to make an example out of her.

⚖

We'll need to go back in time once more. It was during that first September Torts class, just a few short days before the September 11 tragedy, and I was hoping that Doctor McGhee wouldn't call on me. One of the cases assigned to us for that class was *Kennedy v. Parrot*, a 1956 North Carolina case that had something to do with medical consent in a physical battery case. Although I skimmed the opinion a few times, I didn't understand it and just hoped that Dr. McGhee wouldn't summon me. As Doctor McGhee scanned the roll sheet, I noticed her turn the first page over. I was out of harm's way. Or so I thought.

Doctor McGhee called on Lois Stanley to recite the facts of the case. Even at the beginning of our One L year, Lois made herself known as a top scholar. During orientation, she organized her All-Star study group, revered even by upper classmen. The group quickly drafted their case briefs and set their sights on the top spots in class ranking. To no one's surprise, Lois effortlessly recited the facts of *Kennedy v. Parrot*. I kept a sharp eye on the clock that day as I had a fridge full of my favorite beer, Appalachian Ale from West Virginia, waiting for me.

Ten minutes remained after Lois read the facts portion of her group's unblemished brief. Doctor McGhee then spent six minutes asking difficult questions of Lois. Lois countered all of Doctor McGhee's inquiries with clever responses. The volley of Tort knowledge between Doctor McGhee and Lois Stanley was an amazing sight to see that day. Lois was flawless in her rebuttal, but Doctor McGhee boasted no flaws, ever. The wicked Irish devil had the Socratic Method on her side. Lois Stanley, despite her marvelous performance and fine arguments, stood no chance.

Doctor McGhee had enough banter with Lois. Like a tennis pro serving a match-winning ace, Doctor McGhee asked one question to which the clever Celt knew no law student could return a correct answer.

"Ms. Stanley, you seem to have the facts of this case very well memorized, but can you tell us what 'habiliment' is?" Habiliment was a word in the case that had little to no significance in the court's decision. Lois looked puzzled. Doctor McGhee had won. She always won. Lois backpedaled.

"Habili... um... Doctor McGhee, I'm sorry but I don't know." As those fateful words came out of Lois's mouth, I could sense her newly formed study group cringe. No study group was safe from Doctor McGhee's prowess.

Doctor McGhee's face turned as red as the blood boiling beneath her white freckly wrinkled facade. She lifted her cane in the air and slapped it back down on the floor. Lois Stanley recoiled as she probably pictured the same thing the rest of the class did—a bolt of lightning zapping her to oblivion. Lois looked around for help from the folks in her study group. They were too busy trying to find the answer to instant message her. It was too late. Lois was alone and could only listen to Doctor McGhee do what she does best.

Doctor McGhee said softly, "It is a word in the bloody case. I expect you to look in your dictionary and know what every word in every case means or you might as well say, 'I am terribly sorry, but I am not prepared for class.' So Ms. Stanley, what is it?"

Game.

Set.

Match.

We all thought Doctor McGhee would finish Lois off and ride her straight into the depths of academic embarrassment. Doctor McGhee, however, did something worse.

With thirty seconds left in the class period and everyone wanting to escape to safety, Doctor McGhee invoked another facet of the Socratic Method where another student pays for the mistake of the fallen. It was an ugly practice, almost as ugly as Doctor McGhee's mastery of it. Doctor McGhee flipped back over to the first page of the roll sheet, and found some other poor soul to become the victim of Lois Stanley's tedious oversight.

"Mister Burnside!"

My heart raced as I still held on to hope that I was hearing things. As was the case much of the fall semester, I wasn't prepared and was hung over. Doctor McGhee sniffed out my sluggishness. I stood no chance.

"Mister Burnside, please assist your inept classmate and tell me the definition of the word 'habiliment.'" She had said my name twice. There was no escape. Doctor McGhee wanted me as her next victim. I couldn't believe what was happening. I looked around at everyone's face, looked at the clock, and tried to weather the storm.

"Uhhh . . . I'm really not sure, professor . . . it depends how the word is used in a sentence?" Doctor McGhee was too smart to give me a hint.

Doctor McGhee walked up to me within whispering distance. She said softly, "Nice try, Mister Burnside, but it only has one meaning. What is that meaning, Mister Burnside?"

The class went silent, as if it was expecting the start of a bludgeoning. I expected a quick end to what Doctor McGhee was about to hail as my inconsequential existence. But suddenly, an angelic voice echoed between the appellate courtroom walls.

"Doctor McGhee, time is up. We have other classes to go to." Doctor McGhee kept her eye on me for another second and then snapped her head around. It was Portia Simmons, the overzealous suck-up, but in that glorious moment, my salvation.

"Excuse me?" Doctor McGhee hissed, "Who said that?" Doctor McGhee looked at Portia, who was sitting in the front row, dead center. The shrewd professor hobbled over to her and slammed her cane on Portia's closed book. Doctor McGhee couldn't wait to tame the pretentious lectern troll.

I quickly searched Yahoo to discover that habiliment means clothing or apparel. Or it could also mean a characteristic apparatus. I almost searched to make sure I knew what "apparatus" meant, but it was obvious that Doctor McGhee had coveted Portia's discontent when Doctor McGhee softy said to her, "Time is up when I say it is up. For your cute little outburst, lassie, I have a cute little assignment for you. You are to read the next case, and the corresponding problem that goes with it, and give me a five to six minute closing argument for the defense."

Portia's world collapsed.

"But professor, I was just letting you know..."

At this point, I had already quietly packed up my computer and books as my mind was already out the door.

That was a close one.

Then Doctor McGhee quietly, with a benevolent murmur, told Portia more of what she wanted.

"Ms. Simmons, normally in a closing argument before a jury, you would not argue case law. Issues of law are for the judge. But for the purpose of your little assignment, I want you to compare facts in the case that follow the problem on page 62."

Doctor McGhee stepped back, took an ominous breath, and said, "I will see everyone on Wednesday."

Beer-thirty!

As everyone started filing toward the door, Doctor McGhee again slammed her cane on the ground with one more order. We froze. Doctor McGhee once again aimed her viciousness at me and said, "One more thing. Mister Burnside will be doing the same as the plaintiff."

Damn it.

What Doctor McGhee said to me totally didn't sink in until later that day while I was sitting in Property and after I read this instant message from Madison St. John:

> *MaddyPeach22*: Look at Portia's face. She's trying to act so confident and calm. Jeremy, I hope you bury that bitch when you do your closing arguments.

Charlie, in his original goofy manner, pre-September 11th, also sent me an instant message:

> *CHUCKJETSSB*: Yo Slappy, don't choke like the '86 Browns.

After classes were over, rather than going to my apartment and opening my fridge in relief, I went over to the library and opened my Torts book to page 62. The problem Doctor McGhee assigned began with a short statement of facts followed by four pages of questions and answers that looked like they were from a trial court transcript. It was the made-up case of *Saunders v. Petrangelo.*

The case had to do with a wave of robberies that took place in a predominantly working-class, ethnically and racially diverse neighborhood of Central City. Several liquor store employees had been recently shot and killed. The defendant, Salvatore Petrangelo, owned and operated his own liquor store in that part of town. The case arose out of an incident where Petrangelo shot a black man named John Saunders who had entered his store at the height of the liquor store shootings.

John Saunders survived and was the plaintiff Doctor McGhee assigned me to represent. Although I was excited about the opportunity to display what I thought were good public-speaking skills, I knew Portia Simmons was going to be a formidable opponent. She was brilliant, sleekly attractive, and always confident. I was not so brilliant, grungily attractive, and had never felt confident about school. The only way I was going to upstage Portia was to work harder than she did. As Monday evening ended, I read the problem and skimmed the case that we were supposed to use as our legal precedent.

The legal precedent for the problem was *Courvoisier v. Raymond*, an 1896 Colorado case where a storeowner was awakened by a group of people coming through the door of his jewelry store. Although an old case, its facts were similar, sans the black guy.

I skipped all classes on Tuesday except for Legal Process. We were not permitted to miss that class without a doctor's excuse. In Legal Process, I worked on my argument outline. I knew that if I was going to upstage Portia, I had to use an obscure argument to blindside her.

Although I never saw a closing argument other than that of Ben Matlock or Perry Mason on television, I knew it had to sum up the facts in the light most favorable to the lawyer's client. I had a lot of practice to do that night so I pulled my first-ever all-nighter.

Throughout that night, my eyes became bloodshot, my hands shook, and my brain only thought of impressing my classmates. At about 7:00 A.M. the next morning, I poured a cup of coffee, but kept reheating it until 8:15 A.M., when I took my first sip. I was too busy preparing and memorizing. I jumped into the shower and rehearsed while the water ran though my hair.

Although I assumed Doctor McGhee wanted us to look like professionals, I wanted to be myself so I placed the suit I had laid out back in my closet and decided to wear my KISS ARMY baseball shirt along with long camouflage shorts and my loud, clunky sandals. I messed up my hair with the tips of my fingers and refused to shave. I wasn't interested in looking dapper.

I walked to school with my head buried in my notes, trying to memorize every word of my argument. When I finally looked up, I was in the appellate courtroom with Portia Simmons right in my face. Portia fired a snide glance at my shirt and looked back up at me.

"You do know we're going against each other today, right?"

Portia placed her hands on her hips. She was wearing a sharp business suit and shouldering an expensive leather tote bag. I placed my hands on my hips and mocked her.

"Yes, of course."

"Well, I was just wondering," Portia replied, "because you look like you just came from a frat party still drunk."

"All of my suits are at the cleaners and my eyes are red because of new contacts I'm trying out."

I didn't wear contacts and didn't think Grundy had dry cleaners.

Portia responded, "Well, I just hate it when I totally mismatch someone. It takes the fun and excitement out of everything."

I stood back, looked at Portia, and grinned.

Portia zapped her right hip into my direction, spun and walked to her perch. As I watched the vulture self-assuredly sit in her first-row seat, I thought about how I was about to get my first dose of true law school competition.

I became excited. I knew my argument well. I wanted to set the first academic standard of excellence. I wanted to kick her ass.

For the first hour of class, Doctor McGhee wielded her Socratic Method wand to teach us the principles of battery and self-defense. I couldn't pay attention to what she was saying because I had a million thoughts racing through my mind.

What if she forgot about the assignment she gave us?

How will the black students react to my closing argument?

Will I do as Charlie said and choke like the '86 Cleveland Browns during 'The Drive'?

"What if?" "How?" "Will I?" These questions started to make me sweat and caused my leg to race up and down faster than a needle on a sewing machine. My nervous twitching knee then hit the table at a bad angle and caused my uncovered cup of coffee to spill. It wasn't a terrible spill, but bad enough to soak my notes.

There were fifteen minutes left in class. I spent much of that time debating whether to present my argument with or without notes. Then, with two minutes left in class, it looked like Doctor McGhee was packing up her books, like she usually did before she allowed us to exit. I thought that either she had changed her mind about Portia and me, or had forgotten about us altogether. Portia, who probably could not stand being forgotten, did what I should have known she was going to do. She raised her hand high. Doctor McGhee stopped packing and talking and gave Portia the evil eye.

"Yes, Ms. Simmons?"

"Doctor McGhee," Portia quipped, "Mister Burnside and I are prepared to do our presentations now."

Doctor McGhee then looked at Portia in awe. She said softly, "Ms. Simmons, I was about to let the class out early, dismiss you and Mister Burnside from your assignments, and enjoy the rest of my day here in beautiful Grundy." Her voice hardened when she sighed and proclaimed, "But, here we remain."

Doctor McGhee pulled her Torts book back out and hobbled over to an empty seat in the second row.

"Mister Burnside, you have the burden of proof. Proceed."

My knees stopped twitching and I began to stand. Doctor McGhee stopped me as I was raising one leg from the sit position.

"Mister Burnside, before you start, and as previously advised, lawyers don't argue case law in front of juries, but for purposes of this assignment, I want you to use the facts and rule of the assigned case in your arguments."

I removed my rear from the seat and moved my other leg from the sit position. I finished standing and abandoned my coffee-soaked notes. I began to walk to the front of the class, one sandal clanking in front of the other. My body was shaking. As I took my position behind the lectern, I stared my class in its collective eye. Then I gave it everything I had.

"May it please the Court, Ladies and Gentlemen of the jury..."

Because the main point of my argument centered on race, I opened with a quote from Martin Luther King, Jr.'s "I Have a Dream" speech.

"We have come here today to dramatize an appalling condition."

I paused and then continued.

"The facts of this case state that a man was shot. That's it, a man. Not a black man, not an African American, but a man. You heard Mr. Saunders, my client and the plaintiff in this case, testify that he ran through the rain and wind for a late-night refresher. He took time to place his rain gear on. Mister Saunders then made two mistakes. Number one, he turned around. Number two, he showed his face."

I went on to discuss what the evidence showed during the imaginary trial, then paused and made eye contact with everyone I could.

"This court has asked me to compare this case with the case of *Courvoisier v. Raymond*. In doing so, I immediately found the most important factor from the facts of that case. It is fear. The rule in *Courvoisier*, which you are bound to follow and apply to this case, is that self-defense can be established if the fears in question were reasonable."

From there, I compared facts involving the fear discussed in the *Courvoisier* opinion. Then I got to the meat-and-potatoes of my argument: "The defendant shot my client, Mr. Saunders, because Mr. Saunders was black."

I paused and looked for my black classmates. I easily spotted Madison. I then searched for Peter O, whom I could not immediately locate. Even that early in the fall semester, Peter O was hit or miss in classes. Madison seemed as though she was on the edge of her seat. The rest of the class also seemed interested, and I hoped Portia was beginning to panic. I continued, with my head held high and my voice beginning to project emotion.

"Folks, can't you see what's happening here? This is not a situation where the defendant believed that Mr. Saunders would harm him. This is a travesty where Mr. Saunders was black and the defendant shot him because of prejudice, not because of fear. Now you have a choice. Do you sweep Mr. Petrangelo's prejudice under a rug, or do you make him take responsibility for a ridiculous belief that all black people carry guns and are out to kill?"

I set my hands on the lectern and looked down. I then lifted them and my head simultaneously, hoping that I had established credibility with my classmates. I continued:

"Do black people carry guns? Yes, but so do white people. If someone were to come into this building and begin shooting, would it matter what color he was? No*! A gun kills*. An umbrella, the device my client, Mr. Saunders, was carrying the night he was shot, is not designed to kill. The defendant wants you to think that he is fearful of black people, and because of that fear, it was okay for him to shoot my client. The defendant's means did not justify his actions, even if he was afraid. The defendant admitted that he couldn't see very well. He admitted that he didn't want to take any chances. Ladies and gentlemen, the white defendant didn't want to give my black client the opportunity to establish his innocent intent. The defendant didn't want to give my black client the benefit of the doubt. That is not fear. That is prejudice. That is why you should award my client damages."

I was done. I held my head up in the air and strutted back to my seat. The whole class clapped. Peter O appeared in the corner of my eye, without clapping and showing no emotion. I was concerned about the racial element I added to my argument until I saw Madison when I got closer to my seat. She was the last one to stop clapping.

Doctor McGhee was surprised. She lifted her bottom lip over her top lip and nodded her head.

"Decent job, Mister Burnside. Now see what happens when you prepare? Let's see how much your sister in the law, Portia Simmons, is prepared. Shall we?"

I couldn't believe what I had just heard. It sounded like a compliment from the famously critical Doctor McGhee. I wanted to shout out, "No one fucks with the KISS ARMY!" but wisely decided against it. The class started to stir. I looked around and people were whispering things into the ears of those seated to their left and those to their right. Portia Simmons had a tough act to follow.

Portia hesitantly stood up from her seat in the front row. She slowly walked to the lectern. She cleared her throat for what seemed to be three minutes. Perplexity clogged her esophagus. I was eager to see how she was going to contest my arguments and handle the curveball I threw her. Portia began to speak while her nose was buried in her notes.

"Before I begin, I just want to say that for the record, I was not aware that we were being permitted to discuss race in this argument as it wasn't part of the assigned case. I feel Mister Burnside's argument has placed me in an unfair position . . . and I . . . um . . . object?"

Doctor McGhee slapped the bottom of her cane against the wood floor. She said, "Object? Ms. Simmons, he was supposed to place you in an unfair position. Lawyers argue, especially in closing *ar-gu-ments*. Now argue Mister Burnside's points or sit down."

Portia attempted to clear her throat again. She mistakenly stayed in front of the class.

"Mister Raymond, I mean Courvoisier, I mean Petrangelo, had to defend himself from Mister Saunders, who looked like an evil spirit, with his dark face, dark clothes, and dark . . . Okay, and then Mister Raymond, I mean Saunders, because he looked so, dark and you couldn't see a gun . . . that Mister Petrangelo thought he might have . . . Okay, then . . ."

At this point, everyone in the class started to sink in their chairs, except the people who totally despised Portia. Those people were loving every second of her bumbling and were at the edge of their seats.

"The light was bad and . . . When Mister Saunders, I mean Petrangelo, pointed the gun he . . . Just a second, I lost my spot . . . he was fearful that . . ."

Doctor McGhee interrupted Portia, with Portia's face clearly marred with frustration.

"Stop." Doctor McGhee said in her soft iniquitous voice. "Please stop torturing my students. Sit down." Doctor McGhee slowly stood up and reclaimed her sanctified place in front of the room. Portia sat down.

"It seems as though Ms. Simmons didn't want to play lawyer today with Mister Burnside. She could have just stood up here and said nothing and performed at a higher level. Leave now everyone, before I call on someone else to embarrass themselves."

Class was over. Everyone left quickly.

I packed up my notes in my backpack and began walking towards the door. I was proud. As I got closer to the front of the classroom, several of my classmates patted me on the back, gave me high fives, and told me how great they thought I did. Madison was still smiling when she said to me, "You totally reminded me of Matthew McConaughey in *A Time to Kill*!"

As I exited the room, I caught a look of revulsion from Portia. In response, I smiled, pointed at my shirt, snarled, and gave her the rock and roll devil horns sign with my fingers. I felt like a rock star—an attitude I foolishly carried with me the rest of that previous semester.

# Chapter 20

Back in the beginning of the fall semester, I won *Saunders v. Petrangelo* because I employed drama and was confident. My looks got the attention of the ladies (Lois propositioned me for the first time afterwards) and my I-don't-give-a-fuck attitude won over the guys. To win *Burnside v. No Background Checks in Virginia* in the eyes of my classmates that spring, I believed an emotional plea for justice was the only way. While the shootings were fresh in everyone's hearts and the ink was barely dry on the headlines, I knew it wasn't going to be easy to fire up my classmates to leave law school for a week, or more. But nothing was going to stop me from trying.

I stayed up all night that Tuesday preparing for my few minutes before Dickey's class. I prepared the same way I did for my *Saunders v. Petrangelo* closing argument the previous semester.

I pulled my first all-nighter of the spring semester rehearsing what I was going to say. My eyes were bloodshot, my hands shaking and my brain only thinking of one thing: retribution for my inactions involving Peter O. At about 7:00 A.M., I made a pot of coffee and drank every drop by 8:15 A.M. I jumped into the shower and rehearsed while the water ran though my hair.

For this speech, I didn't even consider putting on a suit. I wore my favorite shirt, with camouflage pants. I kept thinking about how perfect the *Saunders v. Petrangelo* closing argument went in September. This time, however, I knew I would not be speaking about a made-up case in a casebook. This was a real issue that could impact real lives. I was ready. I was possessed.

I arrived at the appellate courtroom early and scanned all of the empty seats.

How many will be with me in Richmond?

I sat down in the first row of chairs, bowed my head, and prayed for the second time since September 11. I asked God to give me the strength to find a way to persuade my classmates to follow me.

As my classmates started to filter through the appellate courtroom doors, I paced the area in front of the class, near the lectern. As the room filled, my confidence swelled.

I can do this.

People want to do something about what happened.

People hate guns, but are too afraid to admit it.

This is it.

Dickey walked in exactly one minute late, as he did for all of his classes. I told him I was ready to go. As he began pulling out his books from his fancy leather satchel, Dickey smiled and shook his head in disbelief. He said, "You're still serious? This thought hasn't left your mind yet? Okay, Mister Burnside, you can do this, but I'm going to tell you right now, they're going to think that your idea is preposterous and probably won't listen to a word you say. I just want you to be prepared."

Prick.

Always an asshole.

After my classmates had all arrived, Dickey introduced me to the class:

"Before we begin, Mister Burnside has something to say. I want to let you all know, however, that just because he's up here talking about something, doesn't mean it's what I believe, or what any other faculty member believes. It's his own personal opinion."

A disclaimer? Are you fucking kidding me?

It wasn't Dickey's disclaimer that pissed me off, it was the way he said it: very nonchalantly, seemingly spiteful. I was starting what I thought was the most important speech I would ever give—with one big strike against me.

I took a few deep breaths and looked up. Just as I did in September, I looked at Madison. In September, she hung on my every word. This time, however, she hid her face behind an open book propped on her desk. The vibe from the class was not positive, I thought from the effects of Dickey's introduction. I pressed on regardless, just following President Lincoln's orders.

With a strong voice and my right hand clinched, pounding the lectern, I said, "Appalachian School of Law, a man who had no business with a gun has murdered your leaders. What are you going to do about it?"

I paused.

Silence.

Pointing into the crowd, I said, "The Virginia legislature is still in session. They need to do something about what happened here! We cannot sit idle while our school's name is becoming synonymous with Columbine!"

I paused and tried to look into the eyes of my classmates, but their collective head was down.

Maybe they're just soaking it in.

With powerful delivery and unrelenting might, I discussed how easy I thought it was for Peter O to get a gun. I asked open-ended questions to make my classmates think.

"What happens when another mixed-up student gets his hands on a gun without a background check?

"What happens *when this happens again* with another Peter O?"

I continued my fiery speech, much as I had practiced, but with more intensity and more feeling:

"The Virginia legislature has done nothing to suggest that this Commonwealth's gun laws are flawed. They may be waiting for us to act. A few days ago, State Senator Leslie Byrne cried out for more gun control. She may be waiting for us to ride to Richmond, hold a press conference on the steps of the General Assembly, and tell Virginia that the deaths of Dean Sutin, Professor Blackwell, and Angela Dales were not going to resonate in the media without remedy. If we march on Richmond, she'll have to introduce this bill for us. If we don't tell the media about how easy it is for another crazed gunman to obtain a gun in Virginia, who will? The next set of victims? If we don't act, we will remember this moment as the moment where we could have saved lives, but chose complacency and kept the door open for the next Virginian school shooter."

As I continued, I ignored the disillusioned vibe I was feeling from my classmates. After all, when President Lincoln concluded the Gettysburg Address, he thought his short speech was terrible in light of not receiving applause. Lincoln's

Gettysburg audience was in awe, just as I hoped mine was.

"We have a duty to act! We cannot allow the people of our country to accept and move on from what they are reading in the papers! We cannot allow our friends, relatives and neighbors believe that guns stopped what occurred here—they have to understand that guns created what occurred here!"

I held up the *West Virginia Gazette* front page from January 17.

"Is this what you want ASL to be remembered for? When you go for your first job interview, do you want the conversation to turn to Peter O? Or do you want to be remembered for making a difference?"

I paused, hoping my fellow One Ls would be at least sitting up.

"We should be remembered as former victims who marched on Richmond against the proliferation and easy access to guns and in support of the proposition that students should not have to worry about getting shot when they go to class."

This is supposed to be the moment people are fired up...

Come on, someone cheer for fuck's sake.

"It doesn't stop with us. Do we want to worry about the growing possibility of our kids and grandkids being shot between recess and math class? No! We cannot subject our future generations to the same violence we witnessed here seven days ago! We owe it to them, and to students around the country, to stand and fight!"

It felt like my fellow One Ls couldn't wait for me to sit down. Nevertheless, I announced the time and place for what I hoped to be the meeting to inspire a caravan of protest to Richmond. I saw no one write anything down. I concluded my speech much as I had rehearsed.

"School shootings throughout the country will continue, despite what we do or do not do. But with Senator Byrne's help, we may be able to prevent a future disturbed student in Virginia from obtaining a gun and causing our type of tragedy somewhere else. Join me in taking action!"

Then more silence. I stood and waited to hear something, anything. The overwhelming calm made my head pound like there were cymbals crashing in my ear. After a few more moments of my temple throbbing in anticipation of a reaction, I heard Professor Eisen's voice break the devastating hush.

"Okay now, Jeremy, sit down and let's begin class."

Begin fucking class? After that? I blew my September closing argument out of the water!

We should be piling into cars, ready to take on the world!

When I walked to my seat, shuffling my body behind the chairs of my classmates, they scooted in as far as they could to avoid contact with me, like I had a very contagious disease. When I sat down, I looked around. Still no applause. Still no eye contact. I had an urge to walk right back in the direction of the lectern and zip out the door, never to come back. Had I run, I don't know where I would have gone, but from my experience the thirty seconds before, it didn't matter.

It took a few minutes for me to realize that there was going to be no one magically appearing and yelling, "Let's do it! Let's show the world we won't lie down!" No brave fellow revolutionary was going to holler, "On to Richmond!"

After allowing a moment for me to soak in my apparent failure, Dickey slowly walked up to the lectern. He said, "Well, let's face it folks, Mister Burnside has a fanatical idea. You know where his meeting is. Show up if you want. I'm not going to turn the floor over to pro-gun people as I don't want a debate in my classroom. I let Mister Burnside speak because I wanted to prove to him that it was an untamed idea before he tried to drag ASL into a hopeless cause."

I was steaming.

A hopeless cause?

I was breathing faster and faster and was about to explode.

Why did Peter O have to kill Professor Blackwell, but spare Dickey?

Before I got more carried away with my thoughts, I simmered my emotions by taking a series of deep breaths.

Well, if there was anyone interested in doing this with me before, they sure as hell aren't interested now. Thanks to Dickey.

I was hoping that someone saw through the fog Dickey created to thwart my plan. When class ended, there were no congratulations (or propositions) as there were in September after my *Saunders v. Petrangelo* closing argument. There was, however, an uncomforting feeling from everyone I looked at. No one said a word to me so I decided to refrain from lobbying. I hoped that they really were on board, but wanted to save their support for the meeting. I still wanted to march on Richmond, and hoped others secretly did, too.

I skipped Property II that day. I used that time to seek support from a few former Two L and Three L drinking buddies. I told them of my idea and asked them to go in front of their classes and make announcements about the meeting. One Two L and two Three Ls said they would. I also told Mrs. Frehley about the meeting. She said she would try to be there as well.

When 3:00 P.M. rolled around, the stated time for what I hoped would be a historic assembly, I sat in the trial courtroom with a sign-up sheet, fifty copies of my bill and a few proposed itineraries. 3:05 P.M. came and went—no one. It was soon 3:10 P.M. and I began to wonder if I had clearly stated the date, time, and place.

I was kidding myself. No one was coming; 3:15 P.M. approached and I began to pack my things. The door opened and Todd Criscuola walked in.

Oh shit.

He said, "Where are all of your anti's?"

I continued to pack my things and replied, "What the hell is an anti?"

"Anti-gun, anti-Second Amendment, anti-Constitution, anti-American. You know, 'anti.' "

"I don't know why you're calling *me* an anti. You and the people who believe everyone should carry guns are anti-peace. You all concede to nothing—not even simple little background checks that impose nothing on your so-called 'rights.' And what the hell are you doing here, anyway?"

"Whatever. I was just on my way to my new study group's meeting in the library and thought I might cut through here. Yeah, Lois Stanley asked me to join her group as they had a vacancy left by some pussy who was dumb enough to skip meetings last semester."

Fucking asshole.

"You could've walked around. What are you really doing here?"

"I was going to talk sense into the one or two liberals I thought would maybe show. I wouldn't want anyone from my school going on TV and sounding like you.

But, it seems like no one's here, so, good-bye, fag."

I tried to hold back the disappointment in my face the best I could. I put on my Indians cap and pulled the bill over my eyes. Criscuola left with my pride. I didn't stand up to him as I would sometimes rehearse in my badass voice. As he walked out the west door of the trial courtroom, Madison walked into the room through the east door.

"Hey Jeremy. Sorry I'm late. Tried to convince Charlie to come."

Defeated, and hoping to start off on another topic, I replied, "What ever happened to the KKK coming to Grundy last week? Did you leave?"

She replied, "Shit no. Professor Eisen is a racist idiot and probably just said that to make me and the handful of other black people at this school scared. I just saw Criscuola head this way. Is the meeting over?"

"No. He was here to try to persuade anyone who showed up not to follow me. You know, it really pisses me off that he's been telling everyone that guns saved the day when we all know that's bullshit."

"Yeah, I know," Madison said as she looked like she was going to deliver some bad news. "I also think you should know that Lois was telling people before Property not to come here. She was saying that you went crazy after the fall semester exams and that you're unstable. That's probably part of the reason why there's no one here."

"That fucking bitch!"

She's still pissed that I dumped her! Shit!

"Jeremy, it was a good speech, but you have to admit you've been acting differently since we got our grades."

Changing the subject while looking for some sort of pat on the back, I said, "Did you really show up for the meeting, or did you just want to say that about Lois? I saw you hiding behind your book during my speech."

A tear began to form in Madison's eye. She said, "I was home when my daddy was shot by an angry drunken neighbor. My daddy had a gun to protect himself, or so he thought. The neighbor wrestled it away and, well . . . it all happened too fast."

"I'm sorry, Maddy..."

"So you can imagine how I feel about them. About your idea, I'll go to Richmond if you want me to. Your call for action moved me, but I hid because you were trying so hard and no one was ready for what you had to say. I felt for you."

Looking around the room, wishing a mob of people would come in and be ready to march, I continued, "I guess we're it for the famous trip to Richmond. Wow, what a fucking dumb idea. A statue of Abraham Lincoln told me to do it. Maybe Lois is right. Maybe I am crazy."

At my fifth grade Christmas choir concert, I passed out on top of a bunch of seated kindergarteners during The First Noel, while the lyrics of the song still sung from my mouth. That embarrassment stayed with me for the rest of elementary school. I figured my gun speech would have the same lasting effect for the rest of law school, however long that would turn out to be.

How can I face my classmates after this? Madison seems to think that everyone feels I had a breakdown.

I returned to my apartment and drank hard. It didn't take me long to become drunk and in shambles. I couldn't help but acknowledge that I had more in common with pre-shooting Peter O than I did with my classmates. I was failing out, desperate, went in front of the class and showed that desperation and was viewed as crazy. A few beers after making this realization, I passed out, just like in the fifth grade, but on top of my bed with half-swallowed beer drooling from my mouth.

Hours later, I awoke and opened my eyes to a new motivation.

# Chapter 21

It's a good thing I was on a vision quest. During the fall semester, if I had suffered a similar calamity to that of my spring semester failed march on Richmond, I don't know how, or if, I could have shown my face on campus again. Since I chose to become somewhat of a recluse after ASL placed me on probation in the spring semester, however, I imposed a duty on myself to ignore what I figured others would be saying about me. My quest to find my place in the circle of life quickly returned me to focus. That, and all I needed was a good drunk.

Although I was ready to move on and re-concentrate on my studies, I still had to do something to help me address the one thing that could still distract me the most and cause me to fail: the guilt. When I woke up that morning after my failed gun speech, the solution to that nagging qualm just popped right into my head.

A 5k memorial race.

ASL required each One L to perform 25 hours of community service a semester. During the fall, my project was a 5k race to benefit Professor Blackwell's dilapidated housing repair program, Buchanan Neighbors United. I formed a committee made up of other One Ls, which allowed them the opportunity to piggyback my event to get in their own hours. Having organized 5k races for my fraternity in college, race planning was a cinch for me. Sadly, however, the Neighbors United event stalled after September 11. Charlie was my right-hand man, and momentum for the event died with his cousins.

For the new 5k race, all I had to do was reconvene the committee and just pick up where we left off. Most of the groundwork was already done. Its profit was to go to a new charity, and its intent would be a living memorial. Unfortunately, I was prevented from serving as race director, per Dean Sutin's rule of academic probation where I couldn't hold a leadership position.

Dean Sutin's probation memo said bare minimum extracurricular activities, sole focus on studies.

Shit. I'll figure something out.

Before brushing my teeth that morning, I promptly amended the name of the Buchanan Neighbors race to the *Sutin–Blackwell–Dales Memorial 5k*, changed the date, added pictures of those who died and printed off a few sample race forms. The race form was my prescription script to remedy my regrets.

When I arrived at the library, I opened my Civil Procedure book. The readings dealt with civil complaints and discussed the requirements of this initial pleading. It was a boring read and my attention easily got re-directed to finding a way to make the 5k happen without being the event director. I concluded that I just needed someone who would be willing to take the title and be in the spotlight while I did the work. It didn't take me long to realize that Charlie Vincent was my dude.

Charlie was ASL's direct link to the September 11 tragedy so everyone was already soft on him. Professors left him alone in class. Not even the diabolical Doctor McGhee would call on him. Upperclassmen volunteered to provide him special tutoring and the girls of ASL began to open their eyes to the loveable teddy bear.

Since September 11, Charlie had tried to his best to maintain his cheery personality, but it was obvious that he had lost much inner peace. I believed that being race director would be good for him, convenient for me, and wonderful for the event. Having Charlie in charge also lent credibility to a race where I would likely have trouble gaining support because of my most recent over-the-top tirade, as some were likely describing it.

Before Civil Procedure began that day, I caught the normally charismatic New Jerseyan moping in the Lion's Lounge. I handed him one of the sample race forms and said, "Hey Chuck, feel like doing an old friend a favor?"

Charlie scanned the form and said, "Slappy, you know Lois has everyone thinking you went crazy, right? People are going to think that this is just another one of your nuts-o ideas. You'd better cool it before they kick you out of here."

"Come on, man, you were on my committee last semester. You still need your hours, right?"

"Yeah, but I just figured you stopped this whole race thing. We all we signed up to read to some first graders or some shit."

"Ouch."

"What would you need me to do?"

"I need you to run it."

Charlie patted his belly.

"Look at me, I'm tubby. I can't run three miles."

"No, ass. I need you to serve as the race director."

Charlie smiled and shoved the form back to me. He said, "This is your baby. Maybe this thing can get you thinkin' right again instead of ignoring everyone and making crazy-ass speeches."

Although I was miffed by my closest ally calling my speech crazy, I took Dean Sutin's probation memo out of my bag and handed it to Charlie. I was prepared for his response. While Charlie read, I said, "I hope you can keep what you're reading a secret."

Charlie took a few more seconds to process what the memo meant.

"Holy shit! No wonder you've been so damn quiet! Fuckin' A!"

"Sutin says in there, 'sole focus on studies.' I need it to appear that way so if I don't get off probation this semester, I'll have a better chance with my petition for re-start, if that option is still available."

Charlie grabbed the race form back from me and looked at it again. He then shook his head and placed it in a folder and said, "Alright, if this is the only way I get to talk to you and keep you from doing any more crazy shit, I'll do it. And I won't tell anyone about the probation thing. But you have to tell me what to do."

I shook Charlie's hand and said, "Deal. Thank you. We're going to make a difference."

Charlie started walking away shaking his head. He suddenly turned and said, "Oh, and Slappy, the money has to go directly to the families of the ones who died."

I smiled and agreed.

"Of course. I wouldn't have it any other way."

⚖

With the 5k race set into motion, my Appalachian War extended to another front. I promised myself that organizing it wouldn't cause much distraction. Plus, I had outside support. Charlie became my field general, but I still needed an influential officer and the blessing of a president.

Before September 11, Mrs. Frehley, a former marathoner, had agreed to be my faculty race advisor. At a meeting I had with her shortly after Charlie accepted being director, Mrs. Frehley agreed to reprise her role. In the same meeting, Mrs. Frehley also agreed to become my faculty academic advisor since Professor Blackwell previously held that position. Thankfully, we didn't discuss my failed gun march, as I needed to stay upbeat. After meeting with Mrs. Frehley, I approached ASL's president, Lu Ellsworth, with the new race idea.

President Ellsworth looked more like a scientist than he did a law school president. He had bushy gray hair and a big nose. President Ellsworth also had big, 1970s tinted clunky-looking eyeglasses that made his eyes look smaller than they actually were. I didn't know much about him, only that he played a large role in the integration of the school into the community. The 5k race was a perfect way to stimulate this integration.

When I went to President Ellsworth's office that day, I first spoke to his secretary. Although she was hesitant about cutting into what appeared to be President Ellsworth's lunch break, she introduced me to him. I didn't waste any time. Before I sat down, I immediately began my sales pitch.

"Mister President," I said while President Ellsworth ate a peanut butter sandwich in his cushiony leather chair. "Thank you for meeting with me on such short notice. Let me tell you about an idea I have."

"Jeremy Burnside? Right?"

I nodded.

"I've heard a lot about your ideas. I've heard what you've been saying about guns. It's all over campus. I wanted to tell you that I am quite impressed with your spirit."

"Thanks, Mister President. That means a lot."

"But Jeremy, this just isn't a good time for people to be all riled up. We're all still grieving. You need to understand that."

Pow. He sure as hell didn't sugarcoat that.

I sat back, looked at the floor, and ignored what he said next.

He's probably right.

I really didn't even have a chance to process what had happened in my mind, let alone grieve for those who died.

I wanted action right away.

I didn't really take into consideration how everyone else was dealing with the tragic events.

Probably sensing that I had zoned out, President Ellsworth leaned in and said, "Jeremy?"

"Well, I have to admit," I said as I snapped out of my trance, "that's the first time anyone has really made any sense about why no one appeared like they were listening during my speech yesterday. I really never thought of it that way. You don't think I'm crazy do you?"

"Of course not. We need leaders who promote causes with passion. That's how this country was founded."

"Speaking of causes..."

I handed President Ellsworth a race form and told him about the 5k. He looked over the legal-sized form, smiled, and told me he reviewed my Buchanan Neighbors United fundraiser pitch in September—and liked it. He seemed as though he also really liked the idea for a living memorial to Sutin, Blackwell, and Dales.

"Jeremy, I'm sure the families will greatly appreciate your efforts. This has been such a tough time for everyone. In a few weeks or so, after things calm down a little more, you should begin promoting this."

"Well, actually, Charlie Vincent is the race director. I'm here on his behalf. In case you aren't aware, I'm on academic probation and want it to be clear that I don't have a leadership role."

"In that case, I'll look forward to working with Mister Vincent. But thank you for stopping by and I appreciate your following ASL's requirements."

As I glanced at President Ellsworth before I left his office, I saw it in his face that the events of January 16, 2002, had been especially tough on him. He was at a conference in Richmond when Peter O walked past his office. I suspected President Ellsworth was coming to grips with the possibility that the Richmond conference saved his life.

President Ellsworth took an active role in addressing community grief, instilling educational reorganization, and monitoring the media reactions. He looked worn. Nevertheless, it was his job to keep ASL from coming apart. President Ellsworth's blessing for the race meant a lot.

On the Friday after my failed gun speech, Dickey and Criscuola each intensified their regular sneers and scoffs as I walked past them before Civil Procedure began. Dickey sneered because he must have heard of my meeting with President Ellsworth. Perhaps he thought I filed a complaint against him for sabotaging my gun speech.

Word of the 5k was already spreading and Criscuola scoffed because he probably preferred a memorial to the guns rather than to the victims. At the end of that particular class, I patted Criscuola on the back as I walked down the stairs before he got up from his seat.

Hey fuck-stick, I don't sweat you.

For the next several days, I somehow developed an enemies list, similar to what the NRA does with names of people who preach about peace. I mentally ranked each enemy by the level of threat I foresaw them causing my mission of making Dean's List. If I was to be at war, I figured I had to identify those who I had to defeat.

Dickey took the top spot because I could not only sense him trying to get in my head, but I had to somehow make up for my fall semester D+ in his class. Because the subject matter was so boring and caused me to often drift away, decoding Dickey's Civil Procedure exam was going to be one of my most difficult tasks. But mainly, I wanted revenge for everything he ever said to me. Getting a good grade in his class would be the ultimate retribution.

I also somehow developed a revulsion for Doctor McGhee. Because ASL allegedly forced her to teach Professor Blackwell's Contracts II class, a subject she had never taught before, she seemed angrier than usual. She didn't allow us any cushion for error in our answers after the murders like most of our other professors did. I could sense that she believed teaching Contracts II was beneath her. Doctor McGhee's vindictive and unforgiving Socratic Method seemed that much more diabolical. Contracts II's four-credit prize still made it my key to penetrating Dean's List.

Despite my new ill feelings for Doctor McGhee and her practices, I did enjoy how my classmates floundered in their answers to her questions. As far as I was concerned, my classmates were all cowards from not going with me to Richmond. And I imagined all of them frequently talking shit about me. They also made up the grading curve, which was the main battleground for Dean's List—this made them in my way. After a fall semester of partying with most of them, I trained my mind to regard all of them as expendable and thus wished them failure.

My professors and classmates weren't my only enemies. After the rumors of the KKK lynching Peter O, I felt paranoid of the townsfolk. My northern accent was different from theirs and I drove around town displaying an Ohio license plate. Since I arrived in Grundy, I also could tell that there was animosity from the townsfolk of what they perceived as rich, prissy law students taking over their town for eight months out of the year. I just assumed they despised us out-of-towners. And based upon that simple assumption, I began to loathe them back.

So be it if my professors, classmates, and the townsfolk all hate me—I'll pass this year just to spite them.

I want them to see my name on the Dean's List—published at ASL and in the town paper and I want them to know they didn't get the best of me.

Fuck them.

This distain supplied me another level of momentum, which I believed would carry me through the semester. Whenever I felt like quitting and retreating home, I figured I could just rely on this newfound inspiration to direct me back to battle. With the 5k race, I believed I had good balance.

My motivations stemming from feelings of goodness from the 5k race and vengeance towards my enemies propelled me during the day, but couldn't drown out my nightly feelings of loneliness. It was like I was in a real war sitting around the campfire before a battle, drinking from a whiskey flask and strumming songs of depression. But instead of sitting around a campfire, I stood in my window overlooking Grundy's lighted flood project. Rather than sipping from a whiskey flask, I'd chug at least a six-pack of beer. And instead of strumming a song on a banjo or guitar, I'd yell with the likes of Ozzy Osbourne or Rob Halford of Judas

Priest at full blast on my stereo.

The way I felt inside at that moment is best described from a song from the then-new Judas Priest CD, *Demolition*, lyrics of which I often screamed out my window into the Grundy community:

> Oh look down your noses at me / hating my identity/ Oh but that don't mean a damn thing you see / cause down here in hell everybody loves me.
>
> Hey I know I'm antisocial / cause you act like I'm infected / with some atrocity / and though I know I'm / every bit the same inside / my face don't fit / it's like I got some disease / Oh you keep your face turned away / strip me of identity / oh still got my fortune and fame / 'cause down here in hell everyone knows my name...

# Chapter 22

Thursday, January 31st was an important day in my Appalachian War. It became just a matter of hours before I'd have a new set of days on the calendar. January 16th, which was located in the dead middle of the calendar, would no longer be constantly in my face. Although I knew I would likely carry varying emotions from January 16 into the indefinite future, I was using my studies and my dream of a successful 5k to turn the page. And somehow it seemed to be working as I felt myself academically evolving.

I had already begun outlining my notes to use as a comprehensive study guide for when it would come time to study for final exams. A law student's outline is his or her map to academic success. I threw my fall semester outlines together just days before exams, and my grades reflected that. It became important to me that I began this process early because according to my daily war plan, I was to review my outlines every day. My goal was to be memorizing my outlines while everyone else in the class was typing theirs.

I also started using different fonts and colors to emphasize different rules and case holdings in my outlines. If a professor discussed a rule in class, I would type that rule in red or in large bold font and once printed, highlight the shit out of it. If it was super-important, I typed it in red *and* bold and planned on really highlighting the shit out of it. I used February's first weekend to enter in all of the information to that point in all of my outlines. Just like the difference my handwriting was making to my retention levels, it amazed me how much I was learning about the law just from typing outlines.

Throughout the next week, I continued my outlining and was not only learning the law, but also starting to perhaps love it. Everything we discussed in class all of a sudden interested me. We were covering landlord/tenant law in Property II, undue influence when entering into an agreement in Contracts II, discovery in Civil Procedure II and double jeopardy in Criminal Law. I felt myself wanting to learn everything about these things. And because I wanted to learn more, I actually felt myself starting to understand it beyond what the casebooks or my professors told me about it.

During those magical days, I thrived on being the devoted academic I should have been that prior semester. Each morning, I arrived promptly at the library when it opened. After a hard day of studying and working out at the YMCA, I'd spend the evening in the library until it closed. I wouldn't move from my ASL study carrel in the library until the staff kicked me out. Then I'd listen to my law tapes on my walk home.

But as soon as I opened my door to my apartment every night, my motivation died and I found myself psychologically back to the point where people were telling me that making Dean's List was impossible. Although I felt like I was winning the Appalachian War, I still wasn't totally convinced that Dean's List was possible. Something was missing.

Part of me knew that the motivations holding me together were superficial and could snap at any time. I realized that my newfound disdain for my professors, classmates, and townsfolk wasn't always going to keep me inspired. My budding love of the law certainly wasn't strong enough to lift me out of a growing nightly depression. The question remained as to what would catch me and re-motivate me when all seemed totally lost and I'd fall.

# Chapter 23

I arrived in Cleveland on Saturday, February 9, to see Judas Priest perform at the World Famous Agora Ballroom. Their music was the soundtrack of my Appalachian War and the rip-roaring heavy metal shrills sent electricity to my brain. There was no way I was going to miss their concert, even with my war plan in place.

The Agora had a medieval-dungeon stench to it, a musty aroma with a taste of filth. My concert comrades were drunk, sweaty, and had hair as long as mine. It was a perfect atmosphere for any heavy metal performance. During the concert, I screamed until I lost my voice and my lungs hurt. For the two hours of the show, I wasn't a law student. I was a person.

After the show, and just as the prostitutes and gang bangers started nestling on their respective street corners, I arrived at my dad's house on Marijuana Alley. I snuck softly down to my room, trying not to make any noise. I figured Hammer Mike probably had to load Penelope soon for work. The basement was flooded, like it often was, so I had to walk through puddles to get to my bed. I heard Hammer Mike's incessant snoring upstairs and felt good to be home.

The next morning, I drove to my grandparents' house in Old Brooklyn, located about a mile south of Marijuana Alley and just a few blocks east of comedian Drew Carey's boyhood home. My mom met me there and brought my mail that still came for me at her house. I would have stayed with my mom in her suburban home on the sunnier side of the Cleveland border, but I felt staying with my dad helped us make up for lost time.

While I ate my grandmother's amazing French toast, all my mom wanted to talk about was how I was doing because of the murders. It was like the feeling you get the moments after you're injured and everyone keeps asking if you're okay. You just want people to leave you alone until the pain subsides.

My grandparents had their share of tribulations throughout their long lifetimes.

Growing up in poor Polish immigrant homes during the Great Depression, helping the Word War II war effort, and mourning the death of their first-born son only highlighted what they had to endure. At their age, they spent many of their evenings going to the funerals of their friends. They both sat back and listened to me hesitantly describe how I thought my world might end. With the exception of the murders, my grandparents seemed to be amused with my doom-and-gloom description of my law school experience. Compared to their having to eat unthinkable things to stay nourished during the Depression, my predicament must have sounded like a trip down Sesame Street.

Probably playing off my grandparents' body language, my mom said, "You know Jeremy, things could be worse."

"Yeah, I know. But I can't help it. So much is at stake for me right now."

"Have you been praying like I suggested?"

Without thinking of the repercussions of my answer in a home where Pope John Paul II's picture hung from virtually every room, I said, "Not really."

And that's when my grandmother stopped placing hot French toast on my plate.

Then my mom referenced the fact that I was a Holiday Catholic, going to Mass only on Christmas and Easter. That's when my grandparents' smiles turned to looks of disgust. It was bad enough that I was on academic probation at ASL. By not going to Mass and staying true to what my mom and grandparents tried to instill in me, I felt like I was also on family probation as well.

My mom said, "Jeremy, I know you have your doubts, we all have a little, but you need to believe. What's it going to hurt? It can only help you with what you're dealing with."

Again, dumb to my surroundings I said, "But ma, you have to admit that the Catholic religion, in response to explanations involving logic and reason, tells us to simply believe. That's like when I asked you why I had to do something growing up, you would say, 'Because I said so.' There are no answers there."

My mom smiled at my analogy as my usually pleasant grandparents fumed.

"Well," she said with another smile, "when I would say that, you listened; most of the time, anyway. I tried to set you on a path so that you could learn without telling you why. The same goes for believing—as God doesn't need to give you the answers you seek. You just have to trust Him."

There must have been some truth to what my mom was saying, but I didn't have the patience to listen for it. My mom gave birth to me when she was a teenager in a strict Catholic household. While I grew, whenever Hammer Mike would take off for West Virginia on a "drunk," my mom was left to raise my younger sister and me alone. But my mom always stayed strong. We never missed Mass and she always cited prayer as the reason for her sanity.

My grandfather, a WWII vet and retired union plumber, had a hard time seeing why my prayer pipes were clogged. In his strong, distinct Cleveland accent, he said, "Damn it, that's enough! In my day, we didn't question these 'things' our parents taught us."

Pointing at me with his crooked index finger, he continued, "It's because the people have stopped going to Church and listening to the Good Lord that we have people shooting other people in schools. Now there's going to be hell to pay. You watch. Hell to pay for all of us."

My grandmother giggled at my grandfather's apocalyptic prediction and shook her head. They disagreed on everything. She said, "Jeremy, you at least pray to Mary, right?" My grandmother held the Virgin Mary in such high regard that she believed Mary should be included in the Catholic Holy Trinity, in the place of the Holy Spirit.

With embarrassment, I replied, "Well, Bushi, that's the thing. What I'm trying to say is that I don't pray at all. I should, I know."

Like she had just found the answer to all of my problems, my grandmother shrugged her shoulders and simply replied, "There you are."

After leaving the Romanowski home feeling like a heathen, I drove back to the other part of town. It was early afternoon at Henry's Bar and my dad's rig had suffered yet another setback. Whenever Penelope was down, Hammer Mike got pissed, and drunk. My dad had come a long way since his West Virginia "traipsin" days and was starting to reap the benefits of being responsible. He became a very hard worker, but when his truck was broke, he could only drink beer while others took his loads and made his money.

When I walked in, Hammer Mike was telling his motorcycle-meets-police chase story over by the pool tables. I couldn't hear him, but he had told that story 1,000 times. He liked to brag about running from the cops, but I knew most of it was exaggeration. The barmaid, with sagging tattooed tits and a deep smoker's voice, handed me a beer and called over to my dad, "Hey Mikey, look who's come to see ya!"

Hammer Mike walked over to me, gave me a high five and a strong handshake that lifted me up off the stool. With the smell of several Bud Lights and Marlboro Reds on his breath, he said, "What's up there, homeboy? What brings you to town? You doin' alright?"

"Yeah, I guess. I just needed a break, that's all. Went to see Priest at the Agora last night."

"Cool, cool. Why is it you need a break? It seems like you were just here."

I took a sip of my beer. "I've got a lot going on right now. Trying to stay motivated, you know?"

"Shit, son. You know I'm sorry to hear about what happened down there, but you need to keep your ass in your books. We had a deal. I'm a truck driver. What about you? You a lawyer yet? Burnsides don't take breaks."

I took a few more sips and said, "Hey, I just want to relax a bit. Is that too much to ask?"

"Fuck that. You'll be able to relax all you want when you're dead." Hammer Mike killed his beer when a full can, with the tab open and tilted to the side as his identifier, magically appeared in his hand.

The bar became silent as its authority on life had something important to say. "Listen, a wise man once said that if you ain't drinkin', you ain't gettin' drunk."

"Huh?"

"Son, if you ain't learnin', you ain't gettin' learned."

"What do you mean? I've got a war going, you know, against everyone at school."

"War? What the fuck do you know about a war? Hey dude, I got a line on another tractor and trailer. If you want Penelope, she's yours."

"Yeah. Well, it's just something I've concocted in my head to keep me motivated. I've declared war against everyone around me down there. And no, I don't want to come back up here and be, well, you know . . ."

"What? You don't want to come back up here and become me?"

Fuck.

"Come on, man."

That's exactly what I was thinking.

With a smile on his face, my dad replied, "Fuckin'-A right you don't want to be me. You better not become a mutherfuckin' truck driver. I'd kick your ever-livin' ass."

I smiled back. He continued, "Your mom and me raised you to become somebody. Although your mom and me ain't never been together as much as we should have, and that's my fault, we both always believed in you."

"Dad, I know, but I just have to do it this way."

"This way? Going to concerts and drinkin' beer at Henry's? You have to get tough, son, and do whatever those smart high-fallooters do to get book-tough. And once you've done what they do to get good grades, take your studies to another level."

"I know, but the odds are so against me, you know? I'm on probation.

Hammer Mike said, "Dammit, boy! You can't let those fuckers get you down. Look around . . . the reality of it is that none of your high-falootin' classmates came from a place like this. Shit son, those law students are probably so stuck up, they'd drown in a fuckin' rainstorm."

As I imagined Portia walking through the rain, I chuckled with the rest of the bar. "They're not that bad, dude, but there's truth in what you're saying."

"Well, I *thought* I made *damn sure* my son was no pussy. I think I know what's holding you back. I can't teach you everything, but I will tell you this: You've got to get tougher than a one-eared 48th Street alley cat. Speaking of which, do you remember that time in the alley?"

Borrowing a line from Hammer Mike's arsenal of one-liners, I said, "Is a frog's ass water tight? But I try not to think about getting my ass whooped."

Hammer Mike took a chug of his beer. The folks at Henry's became so attentive to our conversation that they turned off the Hank Williams playing on the jukebox and listened in.

"When you was about six years old, I remember when that ten-year-old tub-of-lard was walking to Sam's over there on Clark Avenue. I gave him a five-dollar bill and said, 'Go fight my son in the gravel parking lot across the alley.' Do you remember what happened?"

"Of course. You paid the kid to kick my ass. Nice father, huh?" The patrons of Henry's laughed. I think I heard one of them say, "That's our Mikey!"

Hammer Mike continued, "Hold on, hold on . . . When you two walked over to the lot, you didn't complain, even knowing what you was up against. You knew you had to do it—because I told you to. And I hope that lesson you learned is now clear."

"But dad, that kid kicked, as you would say, my ever-livin' ass. I understand the lesson learned, but what does that have to do with me being in law school?"

"No, son. I don't think you do understand. You would think that all that schoolin' would make you smart enough to see something so simple . . ."

I interrupted, "Dad, if you're talking about bullies—there aren't many to fight off in law school, just asshole professors. But I can't use my fists, just my brain. If you would've paid that kid five bucks to beat me in a spelling bee or something, I could see how that might've helped me in law school."

My dad set down his can and said, "Son, do you remember what I told you after that kid busted your nose and skinned your knees?"

"Not exactly, just what I remember you re-tell in your bar stories. Were you teaching me to defend my territory?"

Henry's fell completely silent, a rare occurrence. Hammer Mike continued, "No, son, I wanted you to fight that kid and get whooped for a much bigger reason."

"Bigger reason?"

"Come on, think. Well, let me ask you this: When you lived in this neighborhood, after that lard-ass handed you a lickin', you were tougher, right?"

I thought for a moment then said, "I never got beat up, or bullied, if that's what you're getting at."

Hammer Mike slapped my right arm and said, "That's right! That's my point, son. Well, almost anyway."

"I'm getting beat up now. ASL has damn near kicked me out and I kick my own ass when I get down on myself. I just don't want you all to think I have a great shot at passing."

"Bub, I'm talking about your worst enemy."

"My worst enemy is the grading curve."

Shaking his head, Hammer Mike said, "Then you haven't learned anything from that time in the alley."

Apparently, everyone in the bar knew what my dad was getting at but me. A broken down hillbilly from across the bar picked up his head for the first time since I arrived. I recognized the man as one of the West Virginians who had lost his steel job and gained a permanent seat at Henry's. He yelled out, "Well, shit fire and save the matches! Ye ain't never gunna learn nuthin'! Yer worst enemy is our worst enemy! Don't come back in this bar until ye done found it!"

Hammer Mike concurred as he shook his head, lifted his beer in the air in salute and chugged the rest of it down. The broken-down hillbilly's wisdom probably reached its first listening ears in years.

As Hammer Mike firmly patted me on the back, he said, "One day you'll see what I tried to teach you in the alley. I bet it worked, but you're not seeing it yet. You will—but in the meantime, you can't take no breaks and need to keep your ass in the books. Now, as the old man said, go find it on your own. Or don't come back."

# Chapter 24

Returning from Cleveland was like returning to a nightmare left unfinished. Before you fall back to sleep, you mentally prepare yourself for where you think the dream is going to take you. You hope you are strong enough to change the outcome of the nightmare into a happy ending that will forever conclude the terror within your slumber. You close your eyes, see, hear, and smell Grundy, but the nightmare continues.

Different from my previous arrival back to Grundy, I didn't have an eerie feeling—everything was just harsh. All around me, the mountains were putrid. They were brown and rocky with dirt and clay. Bare wood stuck out from the ground where trees and shrubbery used to hide the mountains' daunting appearance. The air was crisply cold. The Levisa River's chilling waters flowed violently through the dark hollers of Buchanan County. Cruel winter clouds shadowed the "Urine Man!" mural. I chose this nightmare.

Late one night soon after I returned, I was working on some outlines and heard someone walk up the stairs to my apartment. People periodically opened the outside door and closed it after they realized that there was no light. The beauty of my new apartment was that there was no working light bulb to illuminate the stairwell, so people had no idea where they were going. This time, however, whoever it was was brave enough to search for the stairs and try to feel around for a light switch. They couldn't have been a guest of Blugg—Blugg didn't want anyone to know where he lived due to his worry of getting served with "papers," whatever that meant.

I could hear the person walk up the stairs the same way I did every day, kicking for the next step before striding. Then suddenly I heard a thud. My curiosity got the best of me and I hurried towards the hallway, guided by my flashlight. I pointed the beam down the stairs and directed the light in the area of some soft moaning.

It was Lois. She had fallen down the stairs.

I ran down towards her.

"Lois, what are you doing here?"

As she tried to get up, she replied, "Well, if you help me up, I'll tell you. You can be sued for shit like this, you know."

I helped Lois up to my apartment. I sat her down on a small futon I had in my study area and took off her shoe. It appeared that she had sprained her ankle. Lois winced as she said what she came to say.

"Jeremy, you look like hell every day. Everyone is worried about you. I'm worried about you."

I fetched some ice from the kitchen, came back and said, "There's no need to worry, Lois. I'm fine."

"But you haven't shaved for like forever. Your clothes and your hair need washing. You live in the library. People who see you at the YMCA say you make loud growling noises when you row on that rowing machine or whatever that weird contraption is. You're a mess. Everyone believes you'll be the next to lose it, if you haven't already."

I wasn't shocked by Lois's comments.

"Well, Lois, I don't give two shits about what people think of me."

Don't tell her about probation. It'll be all over the school, if it isn't already.

As I began to wrap her ankle, Lois grunted.

She said, "Jeremy, when you broke up with me, I thought that you lost your mind because of emptiness in your eyes. I thought you lost it then and I was worried then. But now I'm one hundred times more worried. Getting in front of the class and ordering everyone to protest at the capitol in Richmond? What was that about? People were ready to report you. They thought you were going to pull a Peter O and go on a shooting spree yourself. What were you trying to accomplish? What happened to you?"

I grew upset, stood up and slapped the ice for Lois's wrapped ankle to the floor.

"You know what Lois? Fuck you. Please forgive me for trying to do something about what Peter O did. We could've made a real fucking difference by going to Richmond. I'm still convinced of that. Seriously, have you given any thought to the fact that if Peter O would have never been able to buy a gun, January 16 would've never happened? I know what people are still saying to that. They're saying, 'Well, Peter O would've found a way to kill even if he didn't have a gun.' Those people are fucking idiots. Can you imagine Peter O's puny ass killing three people with nunchucks or an axe?"

Shock etched itself through Lois's face as she just sat, stiff. I wasn't done. I didn't forget what Madison said about Lois's rants to my classmates before Property while I prepared my gun march.

"And another thing Lois, fuck you for telling our classmates that I'd lost it. If anyone were going to report me, it would have been *because of what you said about me* when I was preparing for my meeting. I heard all about it. We'll see who has lost what when GPA's come out for this semester. Tell your entire study group that I'm coming for them. I'm not coming for them in a Peter O way, I'm coming for them in class rank. And tell your new boyfriend, Tater, to kiss my crazy ass. Now get the fuck out of here."

Lois stood up slowly. She said softly, "Wow, you really have lost it. I'll pray for you."

"You do that. I need all the prayer I can get."

Lois left. She left crying and I was left at the top of the stairs pissed off that she distracted me. In the back of my mind, I was tempted to push her down the stairs. It was at that moment when I realized that using hatred to motivate me was causing me to become consumed by it.

She'll pray for me. Ha!

I knew I had to be lonely and isolated from the outside world in order to keep from being distracted. But I didn't want my separation from humanity to cause me to hate life altogether. Help was out there. Maybe Lois was on to something.

But maybe my mom was on to something bigger.

# Chapter 25

Many aspects of Catholicism cannot be fully explained and are accepted mysteries—truths that we can only grow to understand with God's help. Mr. Wood, my seventh grade science teacher, questioned my mostly Catholic class about why things in our religion were the way they were. Although I spoke out against him in class, in the back of my mind I sometimes would give credit to parts of his evolution rants. For example, the Holy Spirit is the third person in the Holy Trinity. I had a hard time understanding why, or more so, how, a mysterious spirit could be God, yet also be separate and distinct from God and Jesus. To me, I doubted whether evolution and Catholicism could co-exist. Science provided clearer explanations, as Mr. Wood said.

In middle school, it never dawned on me that my beliefs could just pick up where logic and reason leave off. As such, I chose Thomas as my Confirmation name, after the doubting apostle. When I left the religious nest of my maternal Polish family, my own spiritual journey throughout high school led me to even more questions and doubts.

Even though I seemingly gave up on the Church, I kept one constant reminder of my completed Catholic Sacraments. Some people have a necklace or a blanket that they feel keeps them safe; I had a miniature picture.

On the second Sunday of the second month of that spring semester, I woke up and looked at my small, plastic print of Jesus that I'd always kept on my nightstand. Ever since my godmother used it to decorate my First Communion cake in second grade, I saw it before I slept and after I awoke. As I got older, I forgot why I felt it important enough to keep so near for so long. That Sunday morning, with hate beginning to dominate my feelings, I gazed at the picture.

Is what I'm doing impossible?

Logic and reason suggest that it is.

But I still believe in Jesus, without any scientific proof that he is the Son of God.

If I accomplish what has been deemed impossible and defy reason, doesn't that lend proof that Jesus is, indeed, God?

If I make Dean's List, logic certainly will be trumped by what my mom has been talking about.

I lay in my bed and struggled with these questions until I looked over at my clock and finally realized that the time had come for me to find out why that little plastic picture was always positioned prominently on my nightstand. So I got up from my bed and decided to go to Mass.

The last, and only, time I attended Mass in Grundy was when the leaves were green and hid the church from the road. It was the service after September 11, when the tiny little church of Saint Joseph's was filled to a capacity of maybe fifty. I only went to Mass because Charlie asked me to before he drove home to his perished cousins' funerals.

When I left for Mass that February morning, I was nervous about how I'd be greeted by the parishioners of Saint Joseph's. It's not as if I could hide in the back of a large metropolitan cathedral and just blend in with everyone else. In the fifteen-pew church, I would stick out like a sore thumb.

When I arrived, a petit Catholic Sister with trousers and a large cross necklace looked genuinely happy to see me. Sister Sofia Caravello welcomed me with a big hug and a bigger smile. Although I had only attended one prior Mass, I knew Sister Sofia from my dealings with the Neighbors United group on my original fall semester 5k idea. In her Appalach-i-fied Italian accent, Sister Sofia said, "Oh Jeremy! It's so nice that you are here! Welcome back!"

"Hi, Sister. Yes, it's been too long."

I sat next to Sister Sofia, who seemed to have taken a keen interest with something on my face. As I knelt to say a few short prayers before Mass began, she placed her hand on my shoulder and whispered, "Your pain is written all over. We'll talk after Mass."

The music then began and Father Joe Cusano, Saint Joseph's priest, approached the altar. When he walked past me, Father Joe reached his hand out and smiled. I shook it and smiled back. I was in a different arena, an arena of goodness. I had been growing accustomed to animosity and anguish.

During Mass, I thought about my family and came to a few significant revelations. The first one was that in addition to not wanting to be Senator Kulick's legislative bitch and my deal with Hammer Mike, I was in law school because of a silent, deeper reason: I wanted to repay my parents for all they had done for me. Watching them continue to fight for grocery money, as they did my whole life, was probably why I chose to fight to enter a profession where I could potentially make a lot of money and make things easier for them.

That set of thoughts led me to think a lot more about my mom and how right she probably was about prayer. For the first time in years, I opened the door to my soul and welcomed the Good Lord in. In those moments at Saint Joseph's, I was discovering what had been missing from my vision quest—and from my life for too long.

During Mass, I recited all of the prayers without missing a beat. Although the lax Appalachian Catholic cerebration was a bit different from that of my methodic Cleveland parish, I knew when to sit, stand, kneel, stand, sit, and kneel, as if I did it every Sunday. The words coming from my mouth and motions of my body made me feel like I was somehow protected. During the blessing at the end of Mass, I bowed my head. When Father Joe said, "go forth," I felt spiritually empowered and ready to take on the world.

As the other parishioners filed out of the church, Sister Sofia directed me to follow her into a back room, where she was putting away the bread and wine. She then crawled up on a chair to reach a book, got down and placed a Bible down on a table.

"Jeremy, God sees everyone's struggles, just like we see them. But God is the only one who hears them when no one is listening, when we're alone. You're alone and I can see that you're fraught with pain. Honey, it's all in your eyes. But I have no idea how or why you seem so besieged. That's between you and God."

An instance of someone looking how they feel.

"To be honest, Sister, the turning point for me was when I wished physical harm on someone a few days ago. I can't feel that out-of-control again. That's why I'm here."

"Why did you feel that way?"

"Well, I think it stems from nearly failing out of school and because ASL placed me on probation. That, and I've been told that it's impossible for me to pass. I mean . . . I even put together an enemies list."

"Oh, Jeremy, an enemies 'list'?"

"Yeah. Anything to stay motivated."

Sister Sofia sighed, shook her head, and continued, "Nearly failed out of law school. Probation. Impossible, they say. Sounds like you're stuck and overwhelmed. That's where your hate is coming from. I have just the thing for you to read."

Sister Sofia opened the Bible, like she knew the location of every word.

"Here."

She pointed to Psalms 69, which read:

> Save me O God for the waters are coming unto my soul.
>
> I sink deep in mire where there is no standing;
>
> I am come into deep waters, where the floods overflow me.
>
> I am weary of my crying: my throat is dried: mine eyes fail while I wait for my God.
>
> They that hate me without a cause are more than hairs of mine head: that they would destroy me, being mine enemies wrongfully, are mighty: then I restored that which I took not away.

I stopped reading and looked at Sister Sofia. She said, "Keep reading. Read all of 69. Start at line 17, read it aloud."

I looked down at the small text and read,

> And hide not thy face from thy servant; for I am in trouble. Hear me speedily. Draw nigh unto my soul, and redeem it: deliver me because of mine enemies. Thou hast known my reproach, and my shame, and my dishonor: mine adversaries are all before me.

Sister Sofia smiled and placed her hand warmly on my shoulder.

"Jeremy, your enemies, or adversaries, are the people who doubt you. They are before you and it sounds like they are mighty. But now as the gospel suggests, draw God near into your soul to stop this flooding of hate. Use your enemies' doubt, not this hate, to deliver you to where it is you wish to be."

And that will fuel me.

For the next four days, I continued to follow my war plan during the day. I continued to go home to drink and bang my head during the night. But when I rested my head on my pillow, I prayed. And when I awoke, I was ready to go forth, stronger than the day before.

By realizing the true reasons why I was in law school, I gave myself something deeper to fight for. By restoring my faith, I gave myself something divine to rely on for those fated moments when I would doubt myself. By adding these two elements to my vision quest, I had strengthened myself not only for final exams, but also for my own personal trials to come.

# Chapter 26

One of my toughest battles of that spring semester took place on Valentine's Day. When I walked into the Lion's Lounge that day, there was a crowd hovering at a table set up between the two wooden lions. One Ls, Two Ls, and Three Ls, alike, were reduced to tears as they read what was written on a bunch of scattered red construction paper. I decided to check it out when no one was around.

Towards the middle of the day and before Contracts II, nobody was at the table—so I walked over. I picked up a heart-shaped piece of red construction paper and read it. I then picked up another and read it. The cards were valentines to us law students. They were intended to let us know that the community was thinking about us on that symbolic day of love. One card read:

> I am sorry for the pain that You are going Through. I hope This Valentine's Day is a Good one for all of you at the Appalachian School of Law. Happy Valentine's Day. Love, Ashley Gibson.

Also on the table with the valentines was a copy of the Valentine's Day edition of the *Res Ispa*, one of ASL's two student newspapers. The *Res Ipsa* read more like a smutty tabloid than a dignified law school newspaper. It featured several gossip columns and allowed students to vent their frustrations on other students and professors in an anonymous fashion.

Someone apparently thought it was a good idea to include me in the Valentine's Day gossip and dedicated the song *Walk Like a Man* to me. I initially shrugged it off because I didn't want to get distracted by reading too much into it.

ASL's published rumor pages weren't gossipy on every page—just most of them. That edition of *Res Ispa* also contained several articles about the strength of the victims of the shootings. Rebecca Brown wrote an article entitled, *A Special Letter of Thanks*... which described how she managed being back at school since being shot. She wrote:

> For I know that no one has been left unscathed by the tragedy we all share, yet the resolve to move on with dignity, strength, and compassion is remarkable and gives me inspiration!

Rebecca Brown was back in class and doing very well. She was happy to be alive. It seemed as though I allowed Peter O's actions to bother me more than Rebecca did. As I read her letter, I realized that if I could develop Rebecca Brown's backbone, I would be just fine.

I had every intention of going back to the library that Valentine's Day evening for a romantic time with my books. Under a dim light, gazing into my casebooks at the study carrel, holding them, learning from them—I imagined it being so intimate. At the YMCA that day, I performed my usual routine. I put on my tight college unisuit, got on the cheap Atari-looking ergometer and I began to row, getting excited for my date with Lady Curricula.

As I yanked on the handle, I noticed a Grundy native peeking into the room I was in, and cracking jokes about me. I saw him in a mirror that he apparently didn't notice. He was quite out-of-shape and had no room to laugh. He then began making jokes about me to his heftier friend, who briefly entered the room to also take a glance at me. I tried to ignore the local, but as I looked more and more at the mirror, I noticed more and more that he was drawing an audience.

Okay Jeremy, no more distractions, just row.

I took a few deep breaths. He then began mimicking my rowing motion.

Ignore the asshole. Row.

I took a few more deep breaths. The redneck then began to mimic my breathing, which caused some of his chewing tobacco to seep out of the corner of his mouth. I tried to think about what type of cases I'd read that night. I tried, but couldn't take my mind off what he was doing.

What a dick. Fuck this.

I got up from the rowing machine and walked into the next room. The local stopped and pretended like he wasn't doing anything.

I said to him, "Hey buddy, pretty funny show. I saw it through that mirror. You were kind of hard to miss."

I pointed at the mirror and the redneck took a passive stance. He said, "Hey buddy, I wasn't referring to you . . ."

"Fuck that, you were dissing me. Who do you think you are, anyway?"

The Grundite then became combative. He looked to his smirking supporters and said, "Nice little outfit. Is that your leotard? Are you going to dance later? Yankee here obviously ain't goin' nowheres for Valentine's Day!"

My blood began to boil. My fists began to clench. A YMCA worker then rushed in and separated the Grundy ogre and me. I was escorted away while the townsfolk laughed. I knew I should've just looked the other way, but his face was just a reminder of what I assumed everyone thought of me.

Walk like a man, they say.

After I left the YMCA, I picked up an eighteen-pack of beer. I drove back to my apartment and tried to listen to some heavy metal to take my mind off my encounter with the asshole from the Y. The more I thought about what he said about me being alone that night, the more I let it bother me. I also thought about being a coward on January 16 and the song dedication. Before I knew it, I was a drunken mess. I had to get out.

At about 9:00 P.M., I walked across the street to see what movies were playing. I pulled my winter hat low over my forehead and wore sunglasses. I didn't want anyone to know it was me. I didn't want anyone to know that I was alone, drunk and depressed on Valentine's Day evening.

I decided to see the new Tom Cruise movie, *Collateral Damage*, because the title reminded me of what could have happened if the NRA had their way and students were armed in the Lion's Lounge at the time of Peter O's rampage. Lots of collateral damage is what would have really happened if panicked students were shooting at Peter O in that crowded area. I thought maybe firing myself up about guns would take my mind off how depressed I was feeling.

I was also hoping the movie would take my mind off women, love, and companionship. I longed to be with the woman I had left to attend law school. But going to the movies didn't work. Happy couples filled the theatre, many from my class. One of those couples just so happened to be Lois and Tater. I desperately hoped to avoid them, but I couldn't stop them from sitting directly in front of me. I sat and watched the movie while sipping on the beers I snuck in, skillfully able to muffle the sound of opening each can. I watched the movie sunk low in my seat and tried not to be detected by the lovebirds in the foreground.

When I returned to my apartment, I consumed the remaining beers and lost myself. After each beer, I stood in front of my window and yelled as loudly as I could. I yelled at my classmates. I yelled at my professors. I yelled at Grundy.

"Fuck you! You're winning now, but you're not going to beat me!"

That Valentine's Day evening ended up being one of the drunkest I'd been in my life. As I sipped my last beer, I faced the Grundy Flood Control Project. My own inner flood prevention project had just begun and therefore was unable to reroute my floodwaters of hate. I pounded on the window and yelled as loud as I possibly could.

"One day, this will all be fucking worth it!"

"I'll have my day!"

"Fuck you all!"

⚖

On Friday, February 15, I woke up and felt the pain of my Valentine's Day. If I hadn't felt that spiritual safety blanket I wove with prayer, I don't know how I would have recovered. I had lost my Valentine's battle, but the Appalachian War continued and I started to feel that overcoming my setbacks was making me stronger.

For the next two weeks, I successfully followed my strict war plan and stayed in exile, taking no breaks just as Hammer Mike commanded. I studied. I outlined. I memorized. Everything was coming together, including the 5k race.

Charlie was doing a great job soliciting volunteers and coordinating the event with the school. I worked behind the scenes procuring donations for advertising and working with the town towards approval for use of Grundy's roads. Charlie and I mostly conferred through email because I didn't want to spend time at meetings when I could've been studying.

We soon changed the name of the event from the *Sutin-Blackwell-Dales Memorial 5k* to the *ASL Memorial 5k.* My idea to march on Richmond may have gone nowhere, but my 5k race plan was flourishing. By the end of February, President Ellsworth promised Charlie and me that the *ASL Memorial 5k* race would be the marquee event during a campus-wide alumni celebration scheduled for the same day. We were starting to sense momentum for the event—not just in school, but also around town and within ourselves.

As February began to end, I focused my efforts on Legal Process. On February 25, my first draft of my spring semester memo was due. Mrs. Frehley developed one fact pattern that we were to use for three major assignments.

The first assignment was a research memo; the second was a motion for summary judgment; and the final was an oral argument based upon the defendant winning that motion. The fact pattern was that of the made-up case of *Cat Chew, Inc. vs. Norfolk Veterinary Hospital.* It was a trademark-infringement case where Cat Chew alleged that Norfolk was using an image in its advertising that was a misuse of Cat Chew's "cat and dog silhouette design." Cat Chew's logo was a black cat silhouetted by a white dog, with both images looking up at a hand. Norfolk's advertisement depicted a white cat with a black dog silhouette. The Norfolk images, unlike Cat Chew's, were looking forward.

Mrs. Frehley assigned me to Norfolk's side, acting as the defendant's attorney. For my position, I was required to argue that there was no likelihood that people would confuse the marks.

I worked for hours on my laptop doing research to prove in my motion that the two marks were "too different for consumers to be confused because Plaintiff's mark created a different effect consisting of an action, more detail, and a different color scheme." I had fun with it and used my imagination to foster my arguments.

Yeah, take that!

Your Honor, the Plaintiff must be blind, in addition to being overwhelmingly stupid, if he can't tell these two marks apart.

And because my guys' mark is so different from the Plaintiff's lame-ass logo, summary judgment should be denied!

Boom!

Up until that point in my law school career, my September closing argument against Portia was the closest thing to fun I had with any assignment I had to do. By working on the Cat Chew case, however, I felt my imagination somehow unlock a previously unused section in my brain that allowed more space for retention. After stacking and storing information in this new hard drive, it was easier for me to access and process it. Before this, I was thinking like a law student and tried to memorize everything. I didn't apply my own common sense. Finally I discovered what Professor Blackwell meant when he talked about thinking like a lawyer.

Memorizing is not thinking.

# Chapter 27

As February ended, I looked forward to March. Peter O had been arraigned and was sitting in jail awaiting his next court appearance. The shadow his evil actions cast over Grundy was beginning to leave. The wounded had all checked out of the hospital and were back in class. The news stories had slowed and the Appalachian School of Law was moving on. And so was I.

I pierced the new month with a glowing dagger of ambition. Although I hadn't yet found myself, I kept adding weapons to my academic and spiritual armories. Prayer, purpose, and persistence were replacing procrastination, petulance, and panic. I was walking tall, in a forward direction and I didn't care that the odds still favored failure. And with my march into March, spring break sprung out of nowhere.

In the weeks leading up to spring break, the gossip winds of ASL blew me information that Lois and Tater were joining many of Lois's All-Stars in California for a vacation. That meant I was going to gain valuable study days on them. A total of six people went, making up five (Criscuola being the lone exception) of the top eight spots in the class. And by my computations, all I had to do was beat one of them to get out of probation.

For my spring break, I planned to continue to follow Hammer Mike's advice and take no recreational breaks. But as I felt myself wear down at the end of February, I knew I needed to give myself at least a couple days away from the monotony of outlining to recharge my batteries. The All-Stars were to be gone five days, so even if I took off a day or two, I'd still be going up at least three study days on them.

I decided to take those few days off beginning on Sunday morning, March 3, and drive to Washington, D.C. to stay with a friend of mine from high school. His name was Dave Gary, a graduate of Gettysburg College and a fanatic of Rufus King, an overlooked American revolutionary-era icon. Dave had just recently started working on his doctorate in history and I believed us to be two in just a handful of people from our high school class to advance beyond undergrad. I justified this social visit with a plan to distribute race forms for the 5k race along the drive while listening to tapes about Civil Procedure and Contracts. So it wasn't a total break.

As I drove to D.C., I slowly watched the bundle of three thousand race forms dwindle away. I distributed the load throughout every rest stop, grocery store, McDonalds, and college campus along Interstate 81. With all my stops, the drive took over eight hours, which meant eight hours of audio lessons and passive learning.

It felt good knowing that people outside of Grundy would view the race forms and see that ASL wasn't dead after the shootings. It also felt good understanding each difficult class topic more and more after each rewind and playback. During my drive, I filled in the blanks of what I'd been reading—all part of my metacognition strategy, or plan to learn how to learn.

I arrived in Washington that late Sunday night after Dave Gary was already asleep. When I awoke, he had already left for work at a museum, so I spent the day distributing the remaining batch of race forms to various D.C. recreation centers while listening to more law tapes via my aging Walkman.

During one tape, a speaker joked about the "look to your left" speech many law school orientation instructors give to anxious first-year students. I bet Dean Sutin did it the best. He said it neither as a joke, nor as part of a One L tradition. Dean Sutin wanted us to understand the grim truth in it—that law school doesn't give a shit about where you came from or who your daddy is—it will fail your ass if you don't embrace it with the utmost seriousness.

Dean Sutin's words usually held more credence with my classmates because of who he was. Pre-ASL, Dean Sutin was heavily involved with a program called "COPS" (Community Oriented Policing Services). It was a program initiated from the Violent Crime Control and Law Enforcement Act of 1994. The goal of COPS was to advance community policing in jurisdictions of all sizes across the country. To achieve its goal, COPS provided grants and training to increase community crime-prevention initiatives.

Reminded that I was running around Dean Sutin's old stomping grounds with a bunch of race forms in his honor, I became certain I could drum up some support for the race and wouldn't just be killing time until Dave Gary got off of work. After dropping some forms off at Dean Sutin's old law firm of Hogan & Hartson, I walked over to his old Justice Department office, not sure of what to expect.

After going through security, I was fortunate to meet many of the employees who worked for COPS when Dean Sutin served as Deputy Director and General Counsel. Many of the folks I met were very happy to know that Dean Sutin's memory would live on with the 5k race. Although no one committed to coming to the event, people who knew Dean Sutin promised personal donations. I felt an increased sense of gratification once I left that office. The *ASL Memorial 5k* was going to accomplish exactly what I had hoped.

As the exciting day became night, I met up with Dave Gary for a few beers and shared stories of our juvenile days. I enjoyed the conversation, but I really enjoyed the companionship. My last conversation about things other than school was with Hammer Mike a few weeks prior when he called me up from Henry's to warn me that the police were still looking for fans who threw bottles on the field in the infamous December 2001 Browns game known as "Bottlegate," an event I was unfortunately a part of. Hammer Mike loved to flaunt his belief that he was "in the know" with his archenemy, the Cleveland Police.

After a good night's sleep, I leisurely browsed downtown D.C. without my Walkman, or any other reminder of what I was battling in Virginia, aside from a few race forms I had folded and kept in my pocket just in case. I went to the biggest of the Smithsonians for the first time and enjoyed looking through America's live history book. I didn't look too hard at the exhibits, however, because I feared that learning something new about history would push out something I had already learned about the law.

Those few hours were so significant to me because I really enjoyed doing what normal dudes do. Beboppin' around town, eating rubbery hot dogs, and checking out girls crossing the street. If only for one morning, I was just a 23-year-old student, without a care in the world. Life seems so much easier when you are just a dude.

After bouncing from tourist attractions, I eventually stumbled upon Pennsylvania Avenue. I missed any type of tour of The White House, but that didn't stop me from trying to get in. Without any crazy expectations, I walked over to a guard shack and approached one of the uniformed brutes.

"Hey man, my school is doing a 5k run for that law school shooting in January. Any way I can talk to someone about whether President Bush would consider becoming an honorary starter?"

The guard smirked, but reached his hand out and pointed to the race form I was unfolding from my pocket. I didn't give it to him until he waved to me to hand it over.

"Thanks. Maybe you can hand it to Mr. Bush?"

Using the same hand waving in the opposite direction, the guard shooed me away.

As I walked off excited about the highly unlikely prospect of George Bush coming to Grundy, I heard a group protesting a few blocks over. So I strolled over towards the commotion. When I got to Freedom Plaza, I discovered that Al Sharpton and some supporters were minutes away from getting on "Freedom Buses" headed to Capitol Hill. They were supporting the No FEAR Act, which an older black woman promised me was a historical piece of civil rights legislation. She said that the bill passed the House, but was stuck in a Senate committee.

According to other people guiding me into one of the buses, I was important to the march and the lives of discriminated federal workers throughout America. Getting on the bus worked to my advantage for two additional reasons: one, I hoped to hand Al Sharpton a race form; and two, it was a free ride in the direction I wanted to go. So I went with them.

It looked as though I was one of the only Caucasian protestors, but I didn't care. I was on an adventure and supposed to be making history. When we arrived at our destination and I disembarked my Freedom Bus that day, someone handed me a sign. It appeared that the group expected me to start taking an active role in the demonstration. Since I didn't know anything about the legislation other than what that one black lady told me, I was afraid someone would sniff me out as a hitchhiker or accuse me of being a spy for the Republicans or something. So after sneaking on Al Sharpton's Freedom Bus and leaving a race form on his seat, I ducked out. I did my part.

On my walk to the congressional office buildings, I finally began to feel a sense of satisfaction with my own protest. When I briefly protested with Al Sharpton, I imagined myself doing what I wanted to do in Richmond about guns. In my mind, I wasn't so much standing up for civil rights workers as I was discovering that there is nothing embarrassing about standing up for what you believe in. Watching Al Sharpton use proscribed racial arguments to advance his message about social inequalities helped me feel less stupid about my taboo gun control speech in Dickey's class.

Sharpton was passionate about his cause for which I was sure people found him crazy. A certain kind of crazy, like Dr. Martin Luther King, Jr. and the resulting success he had with his Freedom Buses of the early 1960s. If their ideas about racial harmony weren't so outrageous, they wouldn't have been so compelling. Surely, I felt, at some point these civil rights leaders experienced the same type of failure I did after my speech about guns. And as that thought passed while I pictured the inspired eyes of the protestors that day, I actually felt proud of myself for taking a chance.

If I hadn't done what I did, I might not have been able to live with myself. I did walk like a man, after all.

When I arrived at Virginia Senator George Allen's office, the receptionist looked at me like I was a homeless man wandering in off the street. After I handed her my last crumpled race form and explained where I went to school, she went into another room and brought out one of Senator Allen's legislative aides. I explained that it would be an honor if Senator Allen would start the race. The aide politely and politically said he would see what he could do.

Nevertheless, it was fun to daydream about hanging out with President Bush, Al Sharpton, and Senator Allen in Grundy. I blissfully imagined that scenario all the way back to Dave Gary's house.

In addition to being a high school classmate of mine, Dave Gary was my cross-country teammate who became a close personal confidant. When he got home from work, we went for a jog around where they were working on the new WWII memorial. I did most of the talking. I told him about the struggles I had with studying, my bouts with loneliness, and told him about my afternoon D.C. adventures. He encouraged me to keep dreaming about my honorary starters, but reminded me of how great it would be if I somehow found a way to become a Two L.

"Burnside, you're going to look back on these days and smile because you're going to experience the same feeling of coming back from way behind in a cross-country race."

"Thanks, dude, but right now I'm definitely not experiencing any runner's high to push me to medal. Just hoping I can finish."

"You will. When finals get close, and you feel prepared, you'll be locked in The Zone."

"I hope so."

"If you pass, just think about the euphoria you'll experience. No one will be able to take such a feeling away from you."

As Dave picked up the pace, I put my head down, revved my arms, and said, "You're right. Damn, that would be nice!"

When I returned to Grundy, I further developed my outlines and added many of the things I remembered from listening to hours of legal study tapes as context. The library closed early every night of break, which gave me some incentive to relax a bit and work on the 5k. Everything seemed to be coming together.

At the end of spring break, I was two assignments ahead in each class and in my outlines. I noticed my new note-taking techniques significantly increasing my retention levels. In addition to the success I enjoyed in my classes scored only by final exam, I had completed my first Legal Process assignment well ahead of the due date.

I was no longer sinking deep in the mire. I was finally standing and was done crying. With things going seemingly right, it became time to ride my newfound confidence to the finish line.

But that was easier said than done.

# Chapter 28

As the spring semester progressed, so did the bushiness of my beard and the girth of my beer gut. The end of March signaled the beginning of the end of my Appalachian War, and with that, the hopeful end of my vision quest. Some days were good days, but despite my personal and academic progresses, many remained bad. There was nothing between. Although I'd sometimes still get down on myself, I was getting stronger.

My looks made me stick out like a sore thumb, but they accurately reflected the depth of the ugliness that my personal journey caused. Just as I did throughout college and through the fall semester, I wore my KISS shirts proudly to class. I still displayed my "Who the F*CK is Eddie Van Halen" concert tee shirt when I went to the store, and I still strutted around campus with a faded Ozzy Osbourne plastered on my chest. Most of my shirts were all black, signifying to me that my life lacked color. All of my shirts began to get increasingly tight—I'd work out for twenty minutes to an hour every day but drank beer from an hour to three hours every night. My Polish grandmother would describe that course as three steps forward, four steps back.

At the beginning of March, I was running up to five miles a day. As the month went on, I was getting faster. I originally wanted to win my age group at the 5k. But as March came to a close, I found myself running leisurely and probably looking like one of those 1970s joggers—hair flopping everywhere, high tube socks, but barely moving above a walking pace.

My drop-off in training mirrored my motivation in school. Final exams were approximately five weeks away. Those five weeks felt like five decades. I wanted my life back. Dating, going out to eat, going to baseball games, and hanging out with friends were all things that I took for granted before that spring semester. Sex was something that I also missed, but I may have missed a simple, comforting hug more. Studying, going to the library, passively exercising and hanging out with myself consisted of everything I did in my new life. And although my vision quest was going much as I had planned, I just couldn't wait for the Appalachian One L I created in myself to die.

⚖

Monday, March 25, 2002, was a big day for me. My final draft of my motion for summary judgment was due to Mrs. Frehley for Legal Process. I had completed it weeks before and turned it in at the beginning of the day without incident. I almost had that important class out of the way.

March 25th was also a big day because it signified the first day of my Appalachian War where I flat-out gave up. I was just about out of the mailroom when I heard Todd Criscuola's voice.

"Burnside's such a little bitch," he said.

One of his cronies replied, "What this time?"

"Today the First Circuit upheld a Massachusetts gun law that restricts gun owners from buying big ass weapons."

"Burnside didn't do anything to cause that."

I could hear Criscuola punching his open palm when he said, "I know, but hearing about this Massachusetts bullshit makes me want to slug that little pussy in the face."

I wouldn't have allowed Criscuola to bother me if I didn't, indeed, feel like such a pussy. I wanted to confront him and tell him that the Massachusetts gun law was supported by law enforcement officials, who should know more about protecting citizens than him or his beloved NRA. I also wished I had the gumption to tell him that he was fucking stupid to believe that average citizens should be permitted to buy high-capacity assault weapons. But I remained silent, hung my head, and went home—just like a pussy. It was like I was so worn down from being me that I lacked any energy to argue.

Before I arrived at my apartment, I used twelve bucks of the $238 I had left to buy the gas station's last remaining case of Bud Light. Realizing I'd run out of money well before I hopefully found a summer job, I wasted the day drinking and sleeping. I wasted the evening, and my voice, screaming out of my window, cussing the world. Other than being so down on myself, I didn't know any other reason why I let Criscuola get to me that day. It was like my previous machine-like attitude short-circuited and I was becoming human again—suffering the human emotion of self-pity.

Before I passed out, I thought about the passages from Psalms Sister Sofia introduced me to. I realized that I still sometimes felt like I was sinking and unable to stand—like that evening when I had a hard time standing because of the booze. I also always felt like my emotions were flooded, never settling. My throat hurt from screaming and my eyes tired from reading. I hoped that the Good Lord was hearing my cries.

Mine enemies were all before me, overwhelming me into another depressed and drunken slumber.

When I awoke the next day, I didn't rush to the library. I didn't read. I didn't outline. I didn't even shower. I just showed up to classes. Late. I took up space in the classroom. Lethargic.

That day in Legal Process, Mrs. Frehley tried to solicit a volunteer to prepare for an extra oral presentation—someone ambitious enough to prepare for both sides without any extra credit. We had an odd number of people in the class and Mrs. Frehley didn't want one person to do their oral argument without an opponent. No one in the class wanted more work without a pay-off, despite Mrs. Frehley's offer to score only the better of the two differing arguments. During her plea, I really wasn't paying much attention and I had my head down, resting on unopened books.

"It seems that Jeremy Burnside isn't challenged enough, so he's going to do it."

I was too dejected to argue. With my head still resting on my books, I just raised my thumb to acknowledge my new task.

Whatever.

Easter was approaching and I was beginning to fall even further behind in everything. I didn't give up anything for Lent other than hope. In the five days from March 26 to Easter, I found myself just going through the motions. I was waking up far later than what was prescribed in my war plan. I did no outlining and didn't listen to my law tapes. I made the excuse to myself that the frequent blasting going on across the Levisa on the flood control project was too distracting. The booms were getting louder, but I could have just stayed at the library longer.

I also stopped running and working out altogether. I drank more excessively and pouted. I'd reverted to my fall semester self in the classroom, surfing the web and playing online chess. When Easter rolled around, I only went to Mass because I had already agreed to read the petitions.

I sat in my usual pew, the third row on the left hand side, facing the altar. Sister Sofia sat with me as she usually did. I paid her no mind. Before Mass began, to make it look like I was praying so I wouldn't have to talk to her, I knelt with my eyes closed, thinking about what time I would open my first beer that day.

Before Father Joe approached the altar to signal the beginning of worship, Sister Sofia grabbed my wrist with one hand and poked me in my chest using the other.

"Jeremy, your soul appears flooded. You smell like rotten beer. I know you're not praying. You close your eyes because of your shame. You can't keep them closed from God."

I felt like I was back in elementary school at Corpus Christi in Cleveland, where I was frequently swatted by the garb-wearing Sisters.

I became angry with the innocent Sister. I broke her grip on my arm, turned to her, and said softly, but harshly, "Sister, please. Let me struggle. Did you ever think that maybe the only thing holding me down in this world is all that mire you keep referencing? Did you ever think that maybe the only thing I now get enjoyment out of is being miserable?"

Sister Sofia's face became red. She turned away from me.

I'm not only losing the Appalachian War, but I'm becoming someone I despise.

Starting with the opening hymn and continuing through the service, I searched for ways I could change. I wanted to go back to being the machine that I was at the beginning of March. I wanted to be motivated. I needed to be motivated. Before I knew it, the church was silent and I was deep in thought. Sister Sofia nudged me. She whispered, "Jeremy, the petitions."

I jumped up out of the pew and approached the lectern. Everyone was staring at me. When I arrived at the lectern and turned towards the congregation, I paused.

I look and feel terrible.

I'm not kidding anyone.

They're not going to listen to the petitions. They're wondering if I've lost it.

I took a breath and then read aloud the petitions of the Church for that Easter Sunday Mass:

> We pray for the soldiers who are fighting against terrorism overseas . . . Lord, hear our prayer.
>
> We pray for the families of those whose gracious lives ended at the law school in January . . . Lord, hear our prayer.
>
> We pray for all students as they approach their final exams . . . Lord, hear our prayer.

The first petition made my heart sink a bit. Those next two petitions almost brought me to tears. Then I continued,

> We pray for those who are alone, that they may keep the Lord by their side and use His company for hope . . .

As I read that petition, Sister Sofia had a tear in her eye and half smile on her face.

> . . . Lord, hear our prayer."
>
> We pray that we keep the Lord by our side when we want to quit . . .

I'm distracted and want to quit.

But I have to do this.

Once I looked up after the pause, the parishioners of Saint Joseph's, each facing his or her own demons, joined together and said, ". . . Lord, hear our prayer."

Hammer Mike, like his dad before him, was an alcoholic. Because of that I didn't drink beer throughout college because I didn't want to become next in the line of alcoholic Burnsides. I cautiously drank my first beer at a fraternity convention at an Indianapolis Hooters after turning 21. I soon discovered that I didn't crave it like my grandfather and dad and therefore gave myself permission to enjoy it.

When I drank during the fall semester of that One L year, I did so to loosen up and have fun. During the spring semester, however, drinking beer took on a completely different meaning once I started to get in touch with my spirituality.

Soon after I initiated my vision quest, I discovered that consuming alcohol stimulated a part of my soul and allowed me to think about my life in ways I couldn't when I was sober. During the day, I was so focused on my studies that I rarely thought about my future. In the evenings, when I would use beer to relax my mind, I appreciated the significance of what I was doing and how I was bettering myself by not quitting. The more I drank, the more I imagined myself as a lawyer. In Native-American vision quests, this type of connecting was done with tobacco and sometimes naked with the medicine man.

Heavy metal also served as a spiritual stimulant for me. The music was dark, and the high opera-type voices connected me to my inner dark side. The sounds of the screeching guitars made the hair on my arms stand up. Lyrics about freedom, unattainable goals, and fantasy opened my mind's eye to endless possibilities for my abilities. With endorphins pumping through my body, heavy metal made me believe that anything was possible, even under the slimmest of chances.

Although I was physically alone, I no longer felt alone in my soul because I knew God was listening. While Peter O awaited his trial to determine whether he'd sit in the electric chair, I thought about how I was preparing myself for my own trial to determine whether I would ever sit for the bar exam. I was entering April with powerful stimulants, balanced with quiet prayer and blessed by the best wingman a guy could have.

My wounds were healing and I was ready to fight again.

# Chapter 29

I only had one day to prepare for my first Legal Process oral argument. It was important to me to show Mrs. Frehley that I had not given up and that I was becoming a mature law student and not a slacker who was just along for the ride. During that day and night, I studied and practiced relentlessly.

On April 2, I woke up and groomed myself for my first argument, but didn't do anything different from any other day. I kept my hair as wild as ever and left my beard the way it was. I wore a wrinkled dress shirt, jacket, stained silk tie, tattered and tight dress slacks, and some old dress shoes. It was just a step up from my camouflage pants and KISS Army tee. I looked at myself in the mirror before I left.

I'm just going to be myself. Looks shouldn't matter.

Even if they did, I know I'll still be more professional than my opponent will.

My April 2 argument was against Bluggton Wayne Carr. I was to argue for the Defendant, Norfolk Veterinary Hospital, with whom Mrs. Frehley decided won on summary judgment for purposes of the appellate argument. Blugg was to argue for the Plaintiff, Cat Chew, Inc. I was mostly familiar with Norfolk's argument because my summary-judgment motion was dedicated to that side. Because this was the assignment that enabled me to use my imagination and start thinking like a lawyer, I knew the material like the back of my hand. I didn't see Blugg as being much competition.

Blugg was not to be denied. He came to arguments clean-cut and wearing a nice suit and a pressed, starched shirt. His scruffy beard may have been gone, but his southern pride was not. The large Virginian warrior presented a flawless rendition of his case, leaving me and the questioning panel of mock judges mesmerized. His typical double negatives were gone and for the first time since I knew him, Blugg sounded like he had a good handle on the English language.

Mrs. Frehley was the only judge on the panel that I recognized. The other two individuals were ASL alums who didn't appear to have read over the competing motions. As Blugg concluded, he walked over to me and whispered in my ear, "Not bad for a good ol' boy, huh?"

I smiled and silently gulped. I was stunned. I didn't think Blugg had it in him. It was my turn. I walked up to the panel, cleared my throat about six times, and froze.

Shit.

Everyone's probably looking at me, wondering if I was going to again say something crazy.

Mrs. Frehley then instructed me to begin. I followed her orders and said, "May it please, um, the, um panel, I mean court . . ."

I stumbled and stopped several times throughout my ten-minute argument. My trembling voice sounded much like Portia Simmons' did when she opposed me back in September. During that first argument, I felt myself saying the same things over and over, painstakingly waiting for my time to be up. I had flashbacks of my gun speech. I felt like I was talking to myself and was not having the fun or confidence I had when I was writing the motion.

After that terrible first argument, I counted my blessings that Mrs. Frehley had volunteered me to present another. If my second argument was better, my feeble argument against Blugg wouldn't count.

I approached Mrs. Frehley afterwards and asked, "Can you tell me who my opponent is for my second argument?" Mrs. Frehley smiled and whispered, "You should know. She's been spying on you this whole time."

I followed Mrs. Frehley's eyes to none other than Portia Simmons.

Shit.

As I opened the door to leave the courtroom, Blugg stopped me and said, "Hey, City. What the hell happened up thair, buddy? From what I've been hairin', you're a damn good spayker. You didn't go and let me win 'cause you git to argue twace, did you?"

So now he's back to sounding like a redneck?

I stopped walking and wished that Blugg had guessed right.

"No, Blugg. I just froze. You killed me. Congrats."

I shook Blugg's hand and walked away.

There was a lot of work to be done before the April 4 oral argument against Portia Simmons. My goal was not to let the name of my opponent psyche me out. I had already beaten her once. But her ace-in-the hole was her spring semester boyfriend. I had a feeling that Todd Criscuola wouldn't allow me to beat his significant other again.

⚖

Seeing Blugg for the first time without a NASCAR shirt or beer cap wasn't expected. I think that Blugg's change in appearance helped him act and sound more like a lawyer and less like a hillbilly. When I presented my argument against him, I didn't feel like a lawyer. I felt like a metalhead dressed as a slacking law student. For my second argument against Portia, I knew I had to do something drastic. When I woke up on April 3, I contemplated the unimaginable: shaving my beard.

For the rest of the day before my second oral argument, I practiced. I practiced hard. I did everything I did when I practiced for my fall semester *Saunders v. Petrangelo* closing argument. I developed an outline. I memorized it. I went to the trial courtroom and recited my appellate argument over and over. I prepared myself for prospective questions from the mock judges.

After ASL locked up and I returned home, I practiced in front of my mirror. As I looked at my appearance, I knew I had to do it. With some hesitation, I picked up my razor and shaved my straggly beard, up to my sideburns. As I erased it from my face with each rough stroke, I began to look younger. I almost forgot there was a young punk under there.

I felt naked. I was worried about how I'd react to people since one major part of the natural veil I grew was gone.

Now I almost look like a lawyer.

I got a few hours of sleep before I woke up to practice more. I thought about how important that day's argument was to my Appalachian War. I needed one of the best grades in Legal Process to have any chance of becoming a Two L, which meant at least a high B against Portia.

As I began packing up my notes, I decided to also brush my hair and pull it back in a ponytail. When I arrived at the trial courtroom, I was ready. Blugg showed up to support me. His beard had already started to grow in and he was back to wearing his favorite Budweiser hat with fishing hook through the bill. Blugg walked over to me and shook my hand. He said, "City, by God, is 'at you? Damn, son, you look like a completely dafferent dude."

"You inspired this, my friend. You did the same thing and kicked my butt. I thought it was a good idea."

Blugg remarked, "Well, I'll be."

Shortly after I turned away from Blugg, I saw what I had expected to see. There stood Portia in her business-like attire and confident facial expressions. With her was my law school nemesis, Todd Criscuola. He stared at me, grinning. I grinned back.

Kiss my ass. Your girlfriend is going down.

The mock judges assigned Portia and me adjacent tables facing them. Portia had to walk past me to get to hers. As she did, her nose was in the air and her walk determined. When Portia reached her table, I was waiting for her to set up her notes and lay out her cases for easy access, as I did. Portia Simmons had no notes and no cases.

No fucking way.

As I gazed in amazement, Criscuola leaned in from the first row behind me and whispered into my ear, "I have my gun on me today. Does that scare you? Are you afraid of guns?"

I turned to reply to Criscuola and stopped.

He's just trying to get in your head to distract you. Ignore him.

I didn't respond. One thing I couldn't ignore was the fact that Portia was reciting her argument without any visual reference. We were required to be familiar with over twenty cases on trademark law. Portia apparently watched me oppose Blugg to observe what cases I cited and was most familiar with. She had done her homework.

To beat Portia again, I needed to flank her on an issue she couldn't know without the use of notes. I had to throw her off as I did in September when I utilized race to carry my argument. I frantically searched my materials for something, anything, she might not know. I was the first up. I didn't freeze, just took a calm breath.

I'm the one doing the avenging here.

Criscuola, you sack of shit, I'm going to show you what I'm made of.

My short opening remarks were perfect. I continued my argument for Cat Chew as if I actually wrote my motion for summary judgment for that side. The panel of judges for my argument against Portia consisted of Dean Lund and Mrs. Frehley. The third judge was a real judge—Buchanan County's Circuit Judge, The Honorable Patrick Johnson, for whom the Johnson Building was named after and who was also presiding over the Peter O murder case. As I began analyzing cases, the panel immediately bombarded me with questions.

The usually timid Lund strongly cut right to the point. He asked, "Doesn't the use of the name Norfolk Veterinary Hospital negate any type of likelihood of confusion?"

"Justice Lund, that's a good question. My answer is yes, it can. However, name, alone, does not matter as much as what is contained in the trademarks themselves. The most important issue here is the similarity of the marks. The name is overshadowed, and thereby trumped, by the attributes that encompass this issue."

I moved from question to question, fighting for my position as if I had the only right answers for every issue. I passed the blame off on the Defendant, Norfolk Veterinary Hospital, and the astounding similarity its logo had with the mark of my client. Then I shifted gears.

"In *Century 21,* the court of appeals stated that bad intent was established against the defendant because it did not know how it came upon its mark. The court in that case inferred that the defendant should have known about Century 21's mark because of its fame throughout the world."

Judge Johnson shrugged and shook his head up and down. He said, "Bad intent. That's an issue not covered by anyone thus far. Interesting."

Bingo. I knew how I was going to beat Portia Simmons.

After discussing how bad intent was important, I dovetailed this argument with its legal origin: the legislative history of the "similarity of the mark" standard. I remembered reading about bad intent in the legislative history during spring break. Knowing how to research legislative history was all the legal expertise I brought with me to law school—and I capitalized on it.

Since I changed the focus of my argument squarely on legislative history, the panel members, who were all sitting up in their seats, listened intently as I explained why the intent of the legal standard at issue was to protect businesses like my damaged client. My presentation came natural as I felt like I was standing before Chairman Wooton and the judiciary committee, just doing my job. I caught Mrs. Frehley's head bobbing up and down in agreement to each of my arguments.

Before concluding, I looked through the corner of my eye and saw Todd Criscuola leaning in from the first row of seats. He was listening intently to Portia, who was frantically whispering into his ear. The judges weren't paying attention—they were focused on me. Criscuola then exited the room quickly. I knew what was occurring.

Portia didn't prepare any legislative history arguments.

I've got her.

With plenty of time to left to finish, I took a deep satisfying breath and said, "Members of this honorable court, the trial court should have denied summary judgment to Defendant Norfolk because there is a genuine issue of material fact as to whether the marks pass the likelihood of confusion test, which test is now the law of the land. The legislative history of this standard supports this conclusion. Thank you."

After a brief pause, perhaps to force herself to stop smiling, Mrs. Frehley announced, "Ms. Simmons. You're next. Begin, please."

Portia stood up slowly and kept looking out the window. She was waiting for Criscuola to come in and save her. I figured that she probably directed him to run to the library to see if he could find any case law to address my legislative history arguments. Portia kept looking around. The panel started looking to see what it was Portia was searching for.

This is awesome.

After thirty seconds or so of silence, a silence I reveled in, Mrs. Frehley said, "Ms. Simmons, no one on this panel is getting any younger and I have memos to grade, so please . . ."

Portia began her memorized argument with no poise. The confident facial expressions she entered the room with went out the double doors with her besieged boyfriend, Todd Criscuola. As she made her opening remarks, Portia's eyes continued to wander from the panel and towards the doors. Although the mock judges had to have been wondering what was so special about the doors, they began their questioning. Dean Lund opened the questions with a continuation from my argument.

"Ms. Simmons, Mr. Burnside spoke at great length about the legislative history of the similarity of the mark standard. What's Norfolk's position on that issue?"

Portia looked dumbfounded. She glanced at the doors two or three times before she said, "Well, Dean, I mean, Justice Lund . . . I would have to say that . . . actually, the legislative history is not important."

I knew right then and there that I had won. Portia violated one of the cardinal rules of appellate argument: a lawyer never tells a judge that an issue a judge inquires about is not important. The theory behind the rule is that if an issue isn't important to an appeal, then a judge would not be inquiring into its veracity. Portia paid a hard price for violating that rule. The mock judges pounced on her.

All of the panel's questions to Portia were about legislative history. Nothing or no one was able to save her. When Criscuola finally re-entered the room, he knew he had no ammunition for his bewildered girlfriend. Without any legislative history arguments for Portia, he looked frazzled and flustered. Portia had no choice but to prematurely conclude.

Portia Simmons loses again.

When Portia turned to sit down, Mrs. Frehley gave me one last smile and I thought I saw a wink. She smiled because I didn't quit on her. Mrs. Frehley winked because I looked, thought, and sounded like a lawyer.

As my adrenalin was pumping, I couldn't allow Portia and Criscuola's failed scare tactics go without comment. After the panel adjourned, I approached Portia's table where she had begun her verbal attack on her thunderstruck cohort.

I stepped in right when Portia was about to finish, "Todd, how fucking hard was it to . . ."

I said to the both of them, "While you all were tanning and having a good time on your spring break vacation, I was in the library reading about legislative history."

Criscuola quickly stood up and stepped towards me like he was going to strike. He held back. With about twenty people remaining in the trial courtroom, Criscuola shouted, "Well, at least we aren't pretending to be a law student like you."

People remaining in the room stopped what they were doing and focused on what Criscuola was going to say next.

"That's right folks; Mr. Burnside here is on academic probation. Portia will be a Two L at this time next year and he'll be back in the hood in Cleveland washing dishes or selling drugs."

Shit. He saw Dean Sutin's probation memo after I had dropped it on the mailroom floor, when I was frantic at the beginning of the semester."

I wanted to tackle Todd Criscuola, but my embarrassment steered me out the door.

I should've kept my damn mouth shut and just left.

Fuck.

# Chapter 30

Charlie and I slated the inaugural *ASL Memorial 5k* to start on Saturday, April 13, 2002, at 8:30 A.M. Most aspects of the race, including advertisement, entertainment, and awards were coming together nicely. One of the most important goals of planning a 5k is ensuring you have an accurate racecourse. We needed a course that was easy and as close to 3.1 miles as Grundily possible. Competitive runners do not like to travel to racecourses that are not the distance advertised. I envisioned the start and finish lines both in front of ASL, but I needed help from Grundy's finest to make this idea a reality.

I had spoken to Grundy Police Chief Barney Stiltner about the course a few weeks prior when I got approval for the race from the Grundy Town Council. Barney was a mild-mannered man, cool as a cucumber. I remember seeing him on campus January 16, bringing Peter O to justice. Barney didn't seek to grab any headlines and I can't remember Grundy's top lawman giving a statement about the murders.

Barney and I met for a run-through a few days before the 5k. As Barney showed me the course in his police cruiser, he was also showing me a side of Grundy to which I had previously closed my eyes. Small-town Grundy may not have had cute little shops, pretty brick roads, or primped trees lining quaint walkways, but it did have a lot of hidden character. Townsfolk waved and smiled at us wherever we drove. It wasn't that "I'm going to wave at Barney so he remembers me when he pulls me over" smile. It was a genuine "Thank you for being around and being Barney" smile. The people who emerged from the closed doors of the beat-up trailers and dilapidated buildings to greet us with genuine "howdys" encompassed what Grundy really had to offer. The benevolent personal sides of these townsfolk, with whom I had not given a fair chance, surfaced.

During our ride, Barney often stopped his cruiser and said the same thing to me.

"Hold on a second, son. I've got to stop here and check on somebody."

About a quarter-way through the course, Barney stopped to simply say hi to a lonely little old lady who was sitting on her porch, waiting for her champion in black. At the halfway mark, Barney stopped to talk to an old-timer sitting in an old lawn chair along Route 460 about some old NASCAR driver. Barney was also a big hit with all the hair stylists in Grundy who were all fans of his television show on public access where he played the banjo. The animated stylists all flirted with Barney and inquired about when he'd be on next playing his bluegrass music.

Grundy's spring had sprung. Leaves were appearing on trees. The flowers around the coal miner statue in front of the courthouse began to bloom. And for the first time since the splendor of Grundy's fall season colored the area, it seemed as though God remembered Grundy and blessed it with beauty.

I traveled around Grundy with Barney for three hours. That's about one hour per mile. Barney could have showed me the course in his police cruiser in ten minutes. I'm glad he didn't. Barney gave me a direct look into the hearts of those who made up the real Grundy, not the Grundy that I cussed at through my window each night drunk before bed.

Grundy's actually a pretty cool little town.

The eve of the *ASL Memorial 5k* was very important. I had met with the committee members earlier in the day and thanked them for the work they had done. I also apologized for not being around. I didn't give an explanation as to why I never attended a meeting because I wasn't sure how fast word spread about my being on probation. Charlie covered for me and told the group I was just a race consultant.

After the meeting, as I tried to dip out so I wouldn't have to hobnob with anyone, Charlie stopped me.

"Slappy, where you going?"

"Just have a lot to do for the race, that's all."

"Come on already, everything's done. Have some beers with me tonight at the luau."

"Hey Chuck, you know what people are saying about me. You also know what I'm up against. I try to limit my distractions, you know?"

Charlie punched me in the shoulder and said, "This race has done a lot for me. It's kept my mind off how shitty this year has been. Beers are on me!"

On that mildly warm April 12 night, one of ASL's legal fraternities sponsored a party in the ASL basement. After I met with the 5k race committee, I planned to go back to my apartment and tie up some loose ends for the race, including getting the bugs out of a computer program I had developed to track racers at the finish using their registration information. I also wanted to stay in and do some mindless outlining so I wouldn't feel too far behind.

However, Hammer Mike taught me many lessons in life, one of which was not to pass up free beer. I could just hear him say something like, "A man who passes up free beer is the type of man to provide no aid to a litter of lost puppies."

I deserve to have a good time. I worked my ass off on this race.

I rationalized that my appearance at ASL that night would be one last way to advertise the race. As such, I put on the *ASL Memorial 5k* tee shirt and left for the party. My appearance at the luau was to be my first appearance at any ASL social function all semester.

After nervously walking to campus, I made my way to ASL's basement classroom, what we called the Dungeon. The ambiance of the Dungeon was dark, cold, and it constantly had a mildewed smell to it, especially after it rained. Its smell reminded me of the Agora in Cleveland. When I arrived at the Dungeon, it was packed.

Everyone at the party stared at me. I wasn't paranoid—they were staring. The way rumors ran around ASL, I wouldn't have been surprised if people were saying that I was crazier than fall-semester Peter O.

Don't worry folks; I'm not going to hurt you. I'm just here to drink some beer with my buddy.

The music was loud and everyone was having a great time. Most people were wearing grass skirts and leis. In addition to my race tee shirt, I wore an inner desire to want to fit in again.

After a frantic search for Charlie, I found him by one of the many kegs. He was already pouring me a cold Appalachian Ale, brewed in Morgantown, West Virginia. As we drank, Charlie and I spoke mostly about the race and discussed contingency plans in case something went wrong with registration or if the weather was bad. When Charlie walked away to mingle with someone else, I hoped he wouldn't try to include me in any conversation. I was worried about how I would interact with others after practically being mute throughout the whole semester.

I didn't have to worry too long as Charlie came right back over and poured my second beer. It was awkward for me to be again drinking with Charlie that night, and in public nonetheless. So much had happened since the fall semester. We were both different people. Although we worked together on the 5k race, we rarely spoke outside of email.

I said to him, "Hey buddy, I just wanted to thank you for all your help on the 5k."

Charlie was watching Madison mingle. He kept his eyes on her when he replied, "No prob, Slap-rod. To me, this run is not just about Dean Sutin, Professor Blackwell, and Angela. It's about my cousins, too."

I didn't know what to say. There was nothing I could say. Charlie and I then just stood, watching everyone else as we went beer-for-beer with each other. It took six rounds of potent ale for me to develop the nerve to open up to him.

"Charlie, I can't tell you how hard this semester has been for me. It's really just changed me into something I'm not."

Charlie turned and said, "What? Are you afraid of becoming a man?"

Charlie squeezed my shoulder and walked away. I stood alone and thought about what Charlie had said. Something told me he wasn't joking.

He's right. I'm now taking responsibility and gearing my life towards a successful future.

I'm doing it.

As Charlie walked towards Madison, I took a few more sips of my beer and began to realize that the Appalachian Ale was playing games with my balance and I needed to leave. There was only one problem. Todd Criscuola was standing at the doors I wanted to exit from.

So I walked to the other set of doors. I looked behind me and sure enough, Criscuola was following me. I quickened my pace and almost made it out of the Dungeon before a strong hand violently turned me around.

Criscuola's angry voice said, "You mutherfucker. Where do you think you're going? We have some unfinished business."

He was fuming. The bully then shoved me with his burly right arm.

I turned to walk away. He grabbed me again.

As a crowd gathered, Criscuola rasped, "Say something, you coward! Or are you too embarrassed now that everyone knows that you're the worst law student in this school!"

I took another step back and said, "Come on, Todd, you're drunk. I've got this 5k tomorrow for the folks that died . . ."

"Oh boo, hoo, hoo," Criscuola said. He became serious when he got in my face, pointed at my nose and continued, "And you would've been dead with them if those boys didn't have their guns pointed at that nigger!" I calmly stepped back to create some space.

"Whatever, I saw Peter O scared shitless. He surrendered because of his own gun—it was out of bullets. You and all of your gun nuts always seem to leave that little detail out."

Criscuola rolled up his sleeves and took the only half step he could back towards me.

"People thought he had more bullets. That's what matters. Maybe I should just beat that in your head!"

The beer in my system was boiling as Criscuola popped my bubble. I tiptoed up to Criscuola's chiseled face so I could be nose-to-nose, then replied, "Just fucking swing then, you backwards-assed piece of shit!"

Criscuola pushed me hard to the floor. I leaped up and got in my wrestling stance, ready to drop-step in for a single leg takedown. There was no way I could beat him in a fistfight.

Suddenly, one of the members of the crowd stepped in front of Criscuola. The tall individual wearing a straw hat and aviator sunglasses caused Criscuola to step back.

"You'd better pick on someone a little closer to your own size."

As the alcohol and anarchy slowed my senses, it took me a few seconds to realize who was under the straw hat. It was Tater Thayer. While looking down on Criscuola, my lengthy former roommate said to me, "Hey Burnside, is Annie Oakley here giving you problems?"

Still in my stance, I replied, "I can't figure out what his real problem is. He's said a lot of nonsense. But clear on out—I want to take him down!"

Criscuola took a few more steps back to create some space. It was my fight and I wanted to fight it, alone—so I countered with a few steps forward, thinking fireman's carry to a knee to the balls while I had him on the floor. Just as I prepared my shot in to grab his left arm and initiate my takedown maneuver, Criscuola wound up his punch. Then, before either of us acted, Criscuola suddenly backed away. He looked to his left and saw Blugg—and then to his right at Dennis Mensinger. Then he looked behind him to see the scrappy Charlie Vincent holding a broken beer bottle. With a hint of stammer, Criscuola said, "Hey you all, your boy Burnside here wants to take away our guns. If you let antis like him keep talking their shit, next thing you know, someone might actually listen! We have rights!"

Tater was not satisfied with Criscuola's response.

"Only cops and pussies carry guns. And with that cute little straw skirt you're wearing, you don't look like an officer of the law."

Criscuola then pushed Tater aside and retreated from the mounting confrontation. As he walked backwards briskly out the door, he yelled out, "Well, fuck you then! If Sutin had a gun, no one but the Africoon would have died!"

With tears in his eyes, Dennis yelled to the gun nut, "Sutin fought his whole life against violence, why the fuck would he carry it with him?"

The skirmish was over. Once Criscuola left campus and we had cooled Dennis off, we all hung out. I drank several more beers with the folks I once again called friends to celebrate. A fight with Criscuola could have taken me from probation to expulsion—and probably to the hospital.

I said to Dennis, "You've always been there for me. You've been a great mentor. And when I become a Two L, I promise to be a better friend."

I spoke just briefly with Blugg and really wanted to talk to Tater.

"Hey Tater, thanks for what you did back there."

"No problem," he said, "I want us to stay buds, okay?"

"For sure. And believe it or not, I'm totally cool with you and Lois. I'm happy for you all."

Tater smiled and said, "Den told me about your damn grades after I cross examined him about what Criscuola's been spreading. When I realized what you were up against, I understood why you left the Johnson Building. I understand who you've become. Lois does, too."

Tater and I hugged and then I stumbled home. I opened the main door to my apartment building and wobbled up the dark stairs. I then felt my way through my door and flipped on the light switch. I looked at my clock. The run was five and a half hours away. I had to be there two and half early. With the room spinning, I collapsed on my bed, hoping to wake up on time.

# Chapter 31

I awoke close to 5:00 A.M. to the sound of my screeching alarm clock blowing ghastly noises into my delicate half-inebriated pounding head. I took a long, hot shower and tried to get rid of the smell of Appalachian Ale that seemed to seep from my pores no matter how hard I scrubbed my skin. Like I remembered doing before the Contracts I final exam in December, I looked in the mirror and experienced the same thought.

I cannot still be drunk. Please. Not on one of my biggest days!

But I was still drunk, or so nervous that I felt drunk. I slowly packed my laptop computer, printer, race materials, and running shoes into my jeep and drove to ASL. I was the first one there. I remembered asking everyone at the committee meeting to arrive two hours early to set up but I also remembered seeing all of the same committee members and volunteers at the luau. The race was to start at 8:30 A.M., sharp. The pressure mounted as it looked like it was going to rain.

I knew I had to pick up the pace. The first person to show up, other than me, was at 7:00 A.M. Charlie came riding in with Madison. Madison walked up to me as Charlie ran into the school.

She said, "Charlie's not feeling so hot right now."

"Damn. We should've left early. Is he going to be okay? You guys left about the same time I did."

Madison leaned in and took a sniff of my body. She grimaced.

"My boyfriend went to bed two hours ago because he kept reciting his pre-race speech without the ability to unite two consecutive sentences. Charlie thought more beer would help him focus. You just witnessed the end product run to the bathroom.

"Charlie's now your boyfriend? Wow. Congrats!"

"Thanks. He may be goofy, but he's mine!"

After about ten minutes, Charlie walked up to where Madison began helping me set up tables. He said, "Hey Burnside, can I talk with you for a second. Alone?"

It was the first time I could recall Charlie addressing me as anything other than something that began with "Slap."

I walked with him to the leaning pine tree next to the marble ASL sign. Charlie sat on the sign and tightened up. I felt a serious conversation coming.

"No, Charlie . . . If you're going to tell me you're backing out . . ."

"No, but I do need to tell you something."

"Sure, anything."

I sat next to Charlie on the sign. He said, "January 16th really messed me up more than I already was. I just allowed you to hide when I should've been your friend. I'm also sorry I wasn't there for you when you made your gun speech."

I gently nudged Charlie's arm and said, "I know exactly what you're talking about regarding January 16th. And about the gun stuff, don't worry about it. Everyone has his or her own opinions. You didn't have to change yours to be my friend. Let's put this behind us and have a good race for those who died on that day."

Charlie smiled.

"Yeah, Slap-turkey, and let's also try to find a way to mask this smell of booze emanating from our bodies. Are you drunk like you were for the fall Contracts final?"

"Maybe a little, but I think I now have enough energy to get through the next few hours. But for you, all of that cologne you're wearing is only going to hide that Appalachian Ale for so long, there, big boy."

I then pointed at Tater, who arrived and was looking quite groggy as he tried to set up the finish line. I said, "Chuck, you might need some of your cologne for that guy, too."

"Shit," Charlie said with a smile, "Try the whole damn 5k staff."

By 7:45 A.M., more volunteers showed up, many suffering the same effects I was, along with Tater and Charlie, from the potent Morgantown brew. Because of my aroma, I tried to keep my distance from many of the church-going ASL

community members who began to trickle in to register to run or walk. I set up my computer and showed some of the volunteers how to work the registration program while I planned on racing. No one understood how to work the database, so I began a short panic.

Damn it. I should've briefed someone on this before today.

Admissions secretary Regina Sweeny was my saving grace. When she arrived and looked at me struggling to explain how the database worked to others, she smiled and sat down next to me.

"Hey honey," Regina said pleasantly. "You sure did have a good time last night, huh?"

"Huh?"

Acting especially chipper, Regina said, "I sure can tell!"

Before I knew it, the line to register was fifteen to twenty people deep. Luckily, Regina took control. I left the registration table on several occasions to check on other things such as the banjo players, nurse's station, and Barney Stiltner's traffic-directing crew. When I approached Barney to ensure that everything with the course was taken care of, he started laughing.

"Mornin' there, Cleveland. I heard there was some drama here at the law school last night. Your name somehow was involved."

A chill ran down my spine and I responded hesitantly.

"Me? How did my name get brought up?"

Barney laughed again and stepped out of his cruiser.

"I'm glad you had a good time. This is some event you got goin' here. Probably goin' to be bigger than the annual Kiwanis run. I'm goin' to go position my boys along the racecourse. This whole thing is not bad, for a Yankee, anyway."

"Thanks, Barney. Maybe one day you'll have to drive up to visit?"

"Not too soon, I hope. I was hopin' you'd be around here for a few more years."

"Me too, man. Me too."

Before I got back over to the registration table, I looked over and saw a sea of middle and high school kids marching down the road, advancing on my position. They were from Mountain Mission School, a small private school up the holler, and they were coming in droves.

Mountain Mission sent its students to the race for several reasons. One reason was that many of the kids were good athletes and would be competing in the 5k race to win. Another reason the students came was to cheer on the participants as Professor Blackwell's children attended school there.

As Madison handed the Mountain Mission kids yellow and green balloons, the colors of ASL, to hold along the racecourse, I paused and looked around.

Holy shit, it looks like there are over 300 people here.

As I stood in a daze to admire the gathering, Lois walked towards me. She said, "Are you okay?"

"Yeah. I'm fine, thanks to Tater. You two are good together."

Lois was a little misty-eyed when she said, "Thanks. I'm so sorry about what I yelled at you in your apartment a few months back. I had no idea what you were going through. Forgive me?"

"Sure. Today's a special day. It's hard to be mad at anyone. Well, except for the asshole who kept pouring me that beer last night."

"I saw you pour most of your own beer, silly."

Growing commotion at the registration table grabbed my attention. The more people that pulled into ASL's parking lots, the more I stressed out. The turnout was bigger than I had expected.

After returning Lois's smile, I said, "Sorry Lois, I gotta go."

It was about 8:15 A.M. and the line at the registration table was finally dwindling thanks to the energy of Regina and the timely reinforcement of Nancy Pruitt and Vickie Keene. Over one hundred runners were registered. The volunteers on the course were in position. And Barney was ready to sound the siren on his police cruiser to start the race.

I looked out to the starting line directly in front of ASL's fountain. I saw the families of those who were killed. I saw the survivors of some of Peter O's bullets. There were smiles. From the victims and the victim's families, to the town spectators, these smiles extended to the faces of every other person at ASL that day.

What began as a gloomy day was beginning to brighten up. Light was beaming through the green and yellow balloons. By the time the race was to begin, the clouds dissipated.

Dean Sutin's wife, Margaret, walked with a stroller, pushing their daughter, Clara Li. She walked beside their son, Henry. Professor Blackwell's whole family was entered in the run. His wife, Lisa, had trained over two months to compete in honor of her husband, who was a former marathoner. Angela Dales's daughter, Rebecca, stood with a balloon at the start, anticipating a good walk in memory of her universally loved mother. Friends of those who died came in from all over the country to participate, including some Blackwell kin from Texas. Witnessing what was occurring around me before the race began was only the beginning of one of the most rewarding experiences of my life.

With the race ready to begin, Charlie used a megaphone to deliver his prepared speech about the purpose of the event. The backdrop was muted and the earth stopped spinning as Charlie spoke from his heart:

> Ladies and Gentleman. It is such an honor for me to speak to you today. On January 16 of this year, we lost three of our mentors, friends, and heroes. A classmate and neighbor of ours took their lives in this building behind us. He took their lives, but he could not take their spirits. Dean L. Anthony Sutin, Professor Thomas Blackwell, and student Angela Dales once stood on the stairs I am standing on now to deliver Halloween candy to neighboring children together. They are now delivering a message to all of us from above. Tony, Tom, and Angela are with us today. They are in our hearts and in our souls. They will be with us as the race begins and will guide us throughout their beloved Grundy community. I want you to imagine Tom wearing his marathon outfit running past you when you runners get tired. I want you to imagine Tony walking alongside his daughter's stroller next to you when you walkers walk with your family members. Finally, I want you to imagine Angela standing in the crowd cheering you on. They will be doing that here today through your courage.
>
> I will not speak the name of the person responsible for January 16's events. I will only speak of his failure. He failed to tear this community and this school apart. Buchanan County and the Appalachian School of Law are stronger and tighter than ever. Witnessing what I'm witnessing, and what Tony, Tom, and Angela, are witnessing from above, which includes all of you with your balloons, walking and running shoes, and most of all love—

> witnessing this in front of ASL is the most beautiful thing. It is the most beautiful thing to be in the presence of the things that no one can take away from us right now—peace and resilience.

After Charlie concluded, there was a great silence. A hush so clear that the only sounds I could hear were the streaming water of Slate Creek and the purring of Barney's police cruiser's engine. The world remained stopped.

Beautiful. Neither President Bush, Al Sharpton, nor Senator Allen could have come anywhere close to that.

All life remained still for what seemed to be a full three minutes, one minute for every person we memorialized that beautiful day. When people began lifting their heads and opening their eyes, Charlie again took the megaphone.

"Okay, thank you. Runners, please take your marks."

Charlie again paused and wiped his eyes as each runner waited eagerly for the sirens. Some of them were still dabbing their lashes. He then shouted, "Runners . . . on your mark . . . get set, GO!"

Barney quickly sounded his cruiser siren and an ambulance horn immediately followed. I refused to allow a gunshot start to the race. The runners were off.

Once I heard the sirens, I snapped out of the state of Zen I went into listening to Charlie and thinking of what was occurring in front of me. I quickly ran and sat down at the registration table to get everything in order for the finish. Sister Sofia, who volunteered as event nurse, hustled over to me.

She said, "Jeremy, Jeremy, go on. Get in there! We want to see you run!"

I ignored her. I felt bad, but I didn't feel comfortable leaving the registration table. One minute had passed, then two. At this point, people were gathered around me, cheering me to go. I didn't even have my running shoes or running clothes on.

Regina shouted, "Come on Jeremy, go!"

Vickie Keene added, "We saw you running through town! You've trained! Go on!"

Out of nowhere, Father Joe, who came to give spiritual support to participants, handed me my running shoes and shorts. He said, "Jeremy, go. We'll all turn around as you change."

Everyone around me then showed me their backs as I changed into my shorts and rushed to put on my shoes. I tied my shoelaces, confused.

How did Father Joe know where my shoes were? I thought I left them in my bag in the floor of my jeep. Plus, I don't even remember packing these shorts.

When I finished lacing my shoes, I looked to Regina and asked her, "Can you handle the rest of the data entry?"

Sister Sofia pushed me towards the starting line and said, "Don't you worry about that! We'll all pitch in. Now go and catch up!"

Before I took off, every bit of drunkenness, stress, and exhaustion I had that morning suddenly disappeared. I found myself sprinting through the group of walkers, and gaining on the runners.

I quickly ran up the most difficult part of the race, the hill that went around the movie theater and towards the Grundy library. As I sped through the slower runners, my pace quickened even more.

When I approached the downhill, I received a heavy metal-like shot of endorphins, sending a tingle up my spine and down my legs. I sprinted faster, passing ten to fifteen more runners.

For two more miles, I was able to forget about my vision quest. It didn't matter that I needed to make Dean's List. I thought only of Dean Sutin, Professor Blackwell, and Angela Dales and how they were helping me carry on.

They died, but their spirits continue and give hope to all these people here today.

After running past the back part of my apartment, along the Levisa River and across from the site of the Grundy Flood Control Project, there was a wave of walkers and Mountain Mission kids holding balloons and cheering on all runners. Behind the Grundy police station and along the Levisa River behind town was also the memorial walk turn-around and two-mile mark. As I ran past it, I had more chills run throughout my body. The cheering section sounded like one from a Roman Coliseum.

Tater was posted there. He led the cheer by yelling, "Go Burnside! Go!"

Others yelled out, "You're doing great!" "Breathe!" "You're almost done!"

Although I began the race significantly late, I had managed to catch most of the other 5kers. My hair, which I didn't have time to place in a ponytail, was flying everywhere. My bare chest, upright and proud. As I passed Dean Lund, I turned around just enough to give him a "low five." He was running hard.

I had a little less than three-quarters of a mile left when I caught up to a teenager with floppy hair and awkward running style. I couldn't figure out how the kid was running so fast. It looked like he was wearing basketball shoes and had never run a day in his life.

As I prepared to pass him, I looked over and noticed his profile. It was Tom Blackwell's eldest son, Zeb. I then fell back a bit, considering whether to let Zeb win.

No, Tom wouldn't want that. He'd want me to beat Zeb if I could.

I ran with Zeb for another half mile, at awe with his determination. I had been training for the race and have done many in the past so I could tell if a runner was in pain. Zeb eyes were squinted, he was breathing heavy. I thought I heard him wheezing a bit. But he was not quitting.

In between breaths, I said to him, "Almost done! Come on!"

In the dozens and dozens of 5ks I had participated in from high school through college, my battle with Zeb pushed me harder than I had ever been pushed before. My lungs must have been working on reserve power, as I had never labored for that long in my life.

As Zeb fell back to where I could only see his face out of the corner of my eye, I yelled out while waving my right arm forward, "Last bit! Push it!"

We were in the final stretch, approximately 150 meters from the finish. After I yelled out to him, I saw Zeb close his eyes, put this head down, rev up his arms, and take off. At this point in the course, people lined the road, cheering both of us on. Within ten strides, we were neck-and-neck again. I then closed my eyes and put my head down, digging for whatever I had left in the tank. We only had approximately 50 meters to go and I took my body to speeds I'm sure it had never reached before.

When I opened my eyes and lifted my head, I had ten meters to go and Zeb had already crossed the finish line.

Zeb Blackwell, no more than 14 years of age at the time, sprinted past me and to the finish line with his father.

When I finished, I walked over to Zeb and shook his hand. As I tried not to fall from exhaustion, I said to him, "You're going to do great things in this world."

We were both trying to catch our breath as Zeb simply said, "Thank you."

# Chapter 32

**Saturday, April 13, 2002.**

**10:15 P.M.**

Here I am—the only one in the library, as usual. After the race, Charlie and I cleaned up and I went home and slept. Upon awakening around five o'clock, I came straight here with every intent to get a lot done. I choose to write in this log because I'm feeling depressed when I should be feeling good about what happened today. It's probably just my lingering hangover from last night's drunk, but I feel this way nonetheless.

I felt good up until a few hours ago when people were gathering outside in the parking lot. They gathered here to car pool to the ASL Awards Banquet, being held at Mountain Mission School. After the race, Mrs. Frehley advised me that she'd be presenting me with the ASL Community Service Award for my efforts with the 5k race. I told her I had plans; as if I have a life outside of the library. That award means a lot to me, but it won't mean much sitting on the dash of my semi as I drive crushed steel for Hammer Mike in Cleveland. Once again, I choose to stay here in this lonely room studying to gain an edge over the people having fun.

For the past two days, I've communicated with students, staff, professors, and townsfolk here in Grundy. For the past two days, it's been fun to be a student at the Appalachian School of Law. It was nice talking to people and sharing experiences with them. It was nice drinking beer in public with others rather than drinking alone late at night. Making this social switch back to seclusion sucks.

And now everyone is coming back from the banquet with smiles on their faces. Tater and Lois will be heading to the Johnson Building to snuggle up together. I can see Charlie holding the award he accepted on my behalf. He just kissed Madison on the cheek. They're probably going to sit on his deck and have a nightcap.

My nightcap will be outlining Contracts. Thank God this semester is almost over.

# Chapter 33

At Mass the next day, Father Joe and Sister Sofia solicited applause for my efforts for the 5k. It felt good. While listening to Father Joe talk about forgiveness, I began thinking about those whom I waged war against. As he spoke, I realized that my Appalachian War, the one I'd been fighting rigorously, was against no one but myself. I was my own enemy all along.

At the beginning of the semester, I waged war against my classmates, professors, and the townsfolk of Grundy. But after listening to Father Joe's homily, I placed a lot into perspective. I realized that the manner in which Barney Stiltner and the parishioners at Saint Joseph's helped me with the race caused me to eliminate Grundy's townsfolk from my enemy list. The manner in which several of my old pals stuck up for me against Criscuola at the luau made me realize that my classmates, although my academic opponents, were not my personal villains. And looking back on the way in which Mrs. Frehley supported me the entire spring semester made me realize that my professors were not my adversaries, but more like my drill sergeants—some of them acted tough and mean, but only because they wanted us to achieve.

Just as I superficially motivated myself with vengeance and hate to motivate me, I also played up the doubt from Dennis, Dickey, and Mrs. Frehley. The early doubt expressed from these three people might as well have come from a million different voices, each whispering in my ear every day. I mistakenly took from Psalms that those who doubted me were as many as the hairs *on* my head. But in reality, I created my enemies from three voices I multiplied *in* my head.

Although I was elated to learn these lessons, the bottom line was that the mistakes I made served purposes. The resulting motivations actually helped me get to where I was. My Appalachian War continued—and I knew exactly where my enemy was.

Now is the time to focus on my inner struggles so that I can deliver myself to the Dean's List.

With just over a week left of classes, I finished my outlines. All of them. I read ahead and had already outlined the information contained in all further class reading assignments. To add more context to my outlines, I began reading a Gilbert's study guide Tim Murphy and some others at the legislature chipped in and bought me after they found out I was on probation. After I read each section in Gilbert's, and by using a green ink pen to write in my outlines, I developed a short, comprehensive summary of the material. I planned to compare it to what we would learn in the upcoming review sessions, which vital notes I would write in red ink.

Then I was going to think like a lawyer and put it all together.

The blasting from across the Levisa River continued to get louder, vibrating the things in my apartment. I decided that I would just have to find a way to ignore it because once classes ended, I wouldn't move from my apartment. My apartment was my haven from distraction. And because I planned on not leaving it, I spent most of my remaining funds on food I stockpiled for the rest of my time in Grundy.

On the final day of scheduled classes, I saw Tater standing by a vending machine. I approached him and shook his hand. I didn't say anything to him verbally. Then I saw Dennis hovering around the Lion's Lounge. I went over to him and shook his hand. I took time to thank him for being a good mentor and for encouraging me not to quit, even after he told me I should. I told him how important his advice was to what I was trying to accomplish. I was saying good-bye.

I saw Charlie just before leaving campus that day. I gave him a hug. I told him that I was going into hiding until finals were over and that he probably wouldn't see me. He smiled and said something to me about not choking like the '86 Browns.

I hoped that my good-byes were just for the summer. I hoped to say hello again in August, as a Two L in good standing and as a friend. I hoped to say hello again as a human, with a life, and not the complicated character I had become.

# Chapter 34

On July 29, 1864, victory was imminent for the Union Army. There was nothing stopping the reformation of the United States. The rebels were demoralized, low on food and supplies, and a few battles away from officially quitting the Civil War. But despite the inevitability of a Union victory, U.S. forces were also growing weary of the fighting. A Virginia blast, orchestrated by one of the biggest scapegoats in military history, would send both sides reeling.

President Lincoln demoted General Ambrose Burnside shortly after Burnside hesitantly accepted his commission as the leader of the Army of the Potomac because Burnside lost one of the biggest battles of the war. As the fighting went on, Burnside did, however, become a key Union leader at the Battle of the Crater, located in Petersburg, Virginia, far from Grundy. Before the battle, Burnside wanted fresh black troops to lead an attack on the important landmark of Cemetery Hill. General George Meade, once Burnside's subordinate, but now superior officer, insisted that tired white troops lead the attack because they were more experienced.

Burnside was beside himself with Meade's disapproval, but had to focus on a diversion to confuse the Confederate forces. Upon unorthodox military tactical deliberation, Burnside decided to plant explosives in a Union-built underground mine to open up the well-fortified Confederate lines. Burnside directed his officers to draw straws to determine who would lead the attack.

The next morning, July 30, 1864, a colossal crash awakened the weary Confederate troops. The rebels were confused—all according to General Burnside's plan. As Burnside's luck would have it, however, the officer who drew the short straw and led the charge, Brigadier General James H. Ledlie, was drunk. Inebriated, Ledlie led the tired white Union forces into the crater created by Burnside's blast. In an ironic turn of events, the well-positioned Confederates picked off the sitting ducks in the crater.

What was supposed to be the waning moments of the Civil War resulted in more disheartenment for General Burnside and the Union. The fat lady had sung long before, but the finishing touches of a long war halted and misery reignited.

# Chapter 35

After my mid-afternoon workout on April 24, 2002, a colossal crash trembled the earth. I was getting into my jeep outside of the YMCA when I felt a thump of air on my chest. The titanic resonance was followed by thundering aftershock. I sprung my body across my front seat and covered my head.

Was it a terror strike on Grundy?

Somebody trying to break Peter O out of jail?

Did the KKK bomb the jail to bury him underneath it?

When the rumble ceased, I sat up, started my jeep, and sped off in search of answers. I stopped at ASL to find someone who knew what was going on. When I walked into the library, no one was studying. Everyone was wandering around, searching for the same information I was. I asked the desk attendant. She didn't know. I asked people who were sitting by the windows when it happened if they saw anything. Nothing. The only thing anyone knew was that the boom was massive enough to shake seats and set off car alarms.

I decided to get back in my jeep and search for the inevitable commotion. As I stopped at the only downtown Grundy red light, a short distance from my apartment, a worker stopped me and said, "You can't go any further, Sir. Wait at the law school until everything gets straightened out."

"Come on man, I have to get home to polish up some outlines for final exams."

The worker asked where I lived. I pointed above the beauty academy. He shook his head.

"Hey buddy, I hate to be the bearer of bad news, but I'd say you should start looking for a new place to stay."

Are you fucking kidding me right now?

"Dude, I have nowhere else to go."

"I hate to break this to you then, pal, but it looks like you may be homeless."

Homeless?

What the hell?

I looked down Route 81 towards my apartment. There was a large cloud of smoke, as if it came from the grand finale of an Independence Day fireworks presentation.

Finally I asked the worker, "What the hell happened?"

Waving me to turn around, he said, "You'll see soon enough. Now back to the law school."

Overwhelmed, I began to turn my jeep around. That's when I saw Blugg. He was walking towards ASL, coming straight from the dust. I called out to him.

"Hey Blugg, do you know what's going on? What was that boom?"

Blugg paused for a moment, began to speak, and then paused again. I never thought I'd see the Grundy native short on words. After a few more moments, he finally spoke.

"Well, it looks like the Corps done blasted boulders into the town. It looks like a damn war zone. People are a hollerin', ve-hicles are busted, and buildins are ruined. It's a mess. I reckon I'll see you later."

"Whoa, wait, wait!"

"Sorry buddy, I gotta make sure none of my kin was downtown when it happened. My old lady was a-posed to be in the dollar store. Someone told me there were amb-al-ances leavin' thair. I need to find me a phone. I'll yell at ya after that."

In light of the worker telling me I could be homeless, I couldn't wait any longer for a definitive explanation, so I parked my jeep on the road and stealthily moved towards my apartment by ducking behind cars and advancing whenever the worker turned his back. As I got closer and closer to my entrance, the dust seemed to get thinner and thinner, revealing more ambulances, fire trucks, and worried spectators. There didn't appear to be widespread doom or panic like there was in Grundy on September 11 and January 16, but there was an eerie feeling amongst the dust in the warming April air.

I stopped when I saw a boulder the size of a bumper car lying in the middle of the road ahead of me. I looked around, saw more large rocks in windshields of parked cars, in the sides of buildings, and scattered across the sidewalks.

Not more death.

Please.

After gawking at the devastation, I quickened my push to my apartment. I felt like I was stuck in either a bad dream or an apocalyptic raid.

When I got within about ten feet of the door, only one worker remained. I was so close that I could make out "Scooby" on the nametag sewn in his shirt. He was keeping people from entering the building and away from the beauty academy's large broken picture window. Scooby soon sniffed me out and directed me to the other side of a caution-taped line.

"Git!"

I sat down on a curb far enough away from the action that I could stay, but close enough to spot an opening. As I plotted, Blugg showed up and sat down next to me. I said, "Hey man, everything okay?"

Blugg delayed his response to catch his breath. He was frazzled. He took a drink of his 32-ounce cola and said, "Well, I reckon. Was runnin' all over tarnation tryin' to track down the old lady and the youngins. They ain't at the hospital at least. How's our shit?"

"No clue, Blugg. Do you know what happened?"

"Don't reckon I do raught now." As Blugg followed my eyes towards our apartment door, he spotted Scooby.

"Oh, well, I'll be! That's ol' Scoob Fig!" Blugg began to stand, like he was going to call out to the worker.

"Whoa!" I pushed Blugg's shoulder to try to keep him at bay. "Blugg, he's the one keeping me from going and checking to see if our apartments are okay."

"Shit, City, Scoob ain't no harm. I went to high school with him and piddled with a few of his four-whillers. I'll talk to him and you sneak up and see if we ain't got no place to live."

I agreed and Blugg went to talk to Scooby. Once Blugg led him away from the door, I rushed under the caution tape and bolted upstairs. I walked slowly in the dark hallway. After feeling for the doorframe, I pushed open the door expecting my whole wall to be blown out. I looked around the corner of my dining room to ensure there was floor to stand on. I then walked into my bedroom and looked around.

Good.

Nothing.

I raced over to my study area. At first glance, everything seemed fine. I then looked on the floor and there were rocks along with what looked like dirt covering the linoleum. I looked around to see where it came from. I was puzzled, but decided that my apartment appearing livable was good enough for me. I grabbed my laptop and ran down the stairs.

As I opened the door, I saw Blugg gesturing me back in. It was too late. Scooby spotted me, lunged towards me, and grabbed my arm.

"Alright you little sum bitch, I told you not to go up har'. You gon git my ass far'd."

I had to act quickly. I just did what any other first year law student would've done. I pretended as if I knew the law.

"Well, I didn't break any laws. Um, actually, pursuant to Virginia law, this is our dwelling and we have the unabridged right to occupy it and take possession of our belongings. It's section 562.1 of the Code."

With a dumbfounded look on his face, Scooby let go of my arm. He said, "Well, that sounds lak a bunch of bool-shit."

With my head in the air, I continued my bullshit as Blugg snuck towards the curb, struggling not to burst out laughing.

"Well, I'm a law student, I know these things. Does your boss know what *quantum meruit* is?"

You get what you put in.

After we walked away from our predicament, I saw Blugg laughing hysterically, and I couldn't help but to chuckle a little myself.

As we made our way to ASL, I told Blugg that it looked like we'd be okay as I only noticed a little dirt in my place, which was directly across from where we assumed the blast was. Blugg didn't seem overly concerned. He did tell me about how he missed his wife. She was seeking a divorce despite his initial impression that they were just working through a law school-induced separation. Blugg finally told me that he didn't want anyone to know where he lived because he was worried about being served with divorce papers.

"Well, Blugg, maybe if I'm wrong and our building becomes condemned, your wife will have to take you back in."

"I don't reckon so, buddy. She cain't handle my studyin'. Worse, she cain't handle me not brang'n any money home for her and the youngins'."

When Blugg and I arrived at the library, it was nearly full. I sat at my usual study carrel and reviewed my outlines until around 9:00 P.M. Blugg sat a few carrels over from me. He didn't have a computer, so he was diligently writing his out by hand. Blugg could have used one of the library computers, but his style worked for him, and I had learned from our oral argument to never question the tenacious redneck.

The more I thought about Blugg the law student, the more I realized that he was much like me. Blugg didn't care what people thought of him. He was generally a jolly guy; he worked hard, but sometimes seemed to have a chip on his shoulder.

Blugg was doing what I was doing. I was an outsider trying to prove to the Grundy folk that all Yankees weren't stuck-up idiots. Since Angela Dales died, Blugg was the only genuine Grundy local left in our class. He knew that. The former coalminer and daddy of three wanted to prove to our class that he was not just a country bumpkin, that Grundy folk weren't stupid.

Blugg and I left ASL together at around 9:30 P.M. and walked back towards our building. Areas of downtown Grundy were still taped-off. Blugg and I hadn't received any sensible answers about what had happened. The ASL librarians didn't discuss it and our know-it-all classmates each concocted their own theories. Some blowhards originally claimed it was a missile. Others insisted it was an avalanche. The general consensus, however, was that something with the flood control project had gone terribly wrong.

Many were saying that one of the blasts must have "hit a seam." Blugg explained to me that "hitting a seam" sometimes happens if a planned explosion hits an air pocket. I didn't care what happened. I just wanted to know that I could conclude my vision quest, alone, in my safe and secluded apartment, and without further intrusions.

As Blugg and I approached the door leading up to our apartments, Scooby yelled out from the community center's parking garage. He had apparently moved once the onlookers all went home and it got dark.

"Hey! They're sayin' they think ya'll can go back up in har'. Goern' to havta espect more tomorra. But we'll be har' all night monitrin' if ya'll need us."

I walked into Blugg's apartment with him. There didn't appear to be any damage at all. I then walked into my apartment and breathed a sigh of relief when I flipped the light switch and they came on.

I immediately went to my study room to reassess the damage. I discovered that the rocks and dirt that were on my floor came from a boulder that had blown its way through my window air conditioning unit.

I inspected my walls on the Levisa River side. They showed no signs of cracking. It looked like I was in the clear.

Thank you, Lord!

Once I got settled back into my apartment and cleaned up the floor in my war room, I ran a hot bath and lit some candles. I had to relax and refocus after that eventful and stressful day. I stayed in the tub for at least thirty minutes, clearing my head and sorting out my thoughts.

I've got to get an A in Contracts II. That's still the key.

Then as soon as the Contracts exam is over, I have to start memorizing Criminal Law so I have the weekend and next week free for Civil Procedure and Property.

When I got out of the tub, I felt invigorated, ready to fight on. I went to sleep anticipating a strong finish to the semester.

Then I woke up.

My alarm clock said 2:37 A.M. My face was wet as if I had been crying, and my body damp like I had been sweating. The spotlight from the flood project was shining in my room and I smelled burning. The scent was like that of a firecracker that just went off.

Surely I was dreaming. Then I noticed a black something on my ceiling. Then the sound of dripping water, quickening more as I sat up. Then I heard something fall from above and make a splashing noise when it hit the floor.

I stood up in my bed and shouted at the top of my lungs:

"*What the Fuck?*"

The next thing I knew, plaster was hitting my head and water was pouring down with the force of a waterfall all over me, my bed, and my already pond-like floor. The water had a revolting stench and the burning smell became more intense.

"*What the Fuck is going on here?*"

I jumped down from my bed and ran to find a broom so I could attempt to turn on the lights without electrocuting myself. I rushed between different points of my apartment, each area mildly lit from the lights coming from the flood control project.

The flavor of water coming down was making me gag. I couldn't figure out why I smelled something burning while everything around me was under water. I forced myself to wake up from what I figured had to be a dream. I slapped my face every few seconds.

Dammit, wake up!

Wake the fuck up, Jeremy!

I threw on a pair of jeans and a tee shirt. I raced around my apartment not knowing what to do, only that I needed to get out of there. I gathered up that which was most important to me, my outlines, and raced next door.

Blugg was already standing outside by the stairs, holding what appeared to be a long, skinny, torch. Upon closer inspection, it was a pair of burning underwear hung on a mop.

The burning.

He was wearing no pants and what had to be a 4X Alan Jackson country music tee shirt barely covering his ass. As he grabbed me to calm me down, Blugg said, "Damn, City, git a hold of urself, feller!"

*"What the fuck is going on, Blugg?"*

I barged into Blugg's apartment. He had water coming from his ceiling as well, but nothing like the ruin occurring across the hall.

“Shit, Blugg, you’ve got it too! I’m going to load my shit into my jeep. You should get your pickup, too. But for God’s sake, put on some pants!”

I ran down the stairs and opened the door. I stepped into a colossal downpour and sprinted towards where I left my jeep. The rain was so dominating; I could only see a few feet ahead of me.

After I got my jeep, I drove it through the caution tape and parked in front of the busted beauty academy storefront window.

Scooby yelled from across the street, “Hey, war’ yins goern’? Is sumthang wrong in thar’?”

Irate, I threw a rock in Scooby’s direction. I yelled back though the rain, “Your company must have shot out my roof! Everything I have is being destroyed!”

I had no idea what I was going to do next. Since I didn’t have any money for a hotel room, my first desperate plan was to set up my tent on ASL’s campus to keep dry and get some rest. Despite the chaos, I needed to find a way to study the next day.

This week is too important!

I ran back up to my apartment and sprinted from room to room with the aid of only a small flashlight. I was running on adrenaline. I grabbed my laptop, hoping it wasn’t damaged.

Then anger took over my senses when I looked out my former study room window. I wanted to throw something through it. I compromised with a non-violent solution. I took a piece of large drywall that was stored in my closet and wrote a message to the culprits with spray paint I had left over from painting the markers on 5k racecourse.

I wrote, “ASSHOLES: THANKS FOR SHOOTING OUT MY FUCKING ROOF” and propped it above my broken air conditioning unit in my war room. I spelled it out large enough so anyone driving along the Levisa River could see it.

I stuffed a bunch of clothes in a backpack, again grabbed my laptop, then raced back down to my jeep. I left everything else in the apartment for dead. By the time I got down the stairs and looked up, several workers had gathered around, dumbfounded by commotion.

"Can you all close this place up for us before I start kicking each of your asses? You all don't want to fuck with me right now!"

Scooby said to me, "Hey buddy, what do you reckon you are a goern' to do?"

I was so angry, but I tried to stay so calm.

"Please call your boss and tell him what happened. Tell him that I and another tenant have no place to stay tonight."

Through an assault of large raindrops, I saw Scooby open up a flip phone to place the call.

At this point, Blugg had his pickup loaded up with many of his things, including his proud collection of country music CDs. Sheltered in the cab of his truck, he yelled at me, "Okay buddy, I reckon I'm goern' to try to stay with my old lady tonight. What are you goern' to do?"

"I don't know yet. Scooby's supposed to be calling his boss. I was just planning on setting up my tent on ASL's front lawn. I have no money and nowhere to go."

Blugg shook his head.

"Well, City, I'd invite you over my place, but I don't reckon I even know if I'm welcome."

"Thanks anyway. See you tomorrow?"

"Yup."

Blugg sped away through the violent torrent.

After a few minutes, Scooby walked over to the window of my jeep. He was having trouble looking in my direction because of the heavy, potent raindrops that were blocking his sight. He said, "They told me to tell you-ins to go over to a hot-el and we'll fix ye right up. Just save yer' re-ceet."

"Is there one open?"

"Try 'at new Comfort Inn they just done built. If that don't work, come on back har'."

"Okay."

As I was about to pull off, Scooby tapped my window. I rolled it down. He said, "They also done said for ya'll to meet tomarra at noon at the Teen Cenner fir a meet-in' about this. I'll get the message to Blugg."

"Thanks."

For fucking nothing, asshole.

Barely able to see the road from the onslaught of water emerging from the dark night sky, I drove towards the Comfort Inn, Grundy's only bona fide hotel, and the only place I thought had a chance of being open.

As I got close to the entrance to the hotel, I prayed it was open. There were only three cars in the parking lot, so I knew they had rooms available. I was uneasy about my immediate means of payment though, which was none. The door opened automatically and I noticed an attendant behind the desk. I went up to the front desk and placed my slimy, smelly hands on the counter.

"I need a room, please. The engineers will cover it."

I hoped that the engineers would cover it, that is.

The attendant was a younger man, probably just graduated high school. He looked at me with bewilderment and confusion.

"Sorry Sir, I can't help you."

I glared at the young local, who had a severe case of acne and who was trying to hide his eyes behind his thick glasses.

"What do you mean, you can't help me?"

"We're all booked up tonight. Sorry, Sir."

As I stood there, with my long hair drenched in aged debris from my ceiling and water, I realized that I looked like I had just killed someone and needed a hideout.

I said to him, "Hey, listen kid, did you hear of today's shit over at the blast zone?"

The attendant nodded.

"My apartment is full of water and everything I own is being destroyed right now. Now give me a fucking room, for fuck's sake."

The attendant looked down at his computer. He tried to hide his trembling hands.

"Sorry Sir, nothing."

I was sure that no other places were open in Grundy and my jeep didn't have enough gas to make it to the next town of Richlands, Virginia. I had just remembered that my tent was near the electrical box in my apartment, so my original plan of camping outside of ASL was out. I paced and paced, trying to think of what to do. The Comfort Inn was my only option.

After looking outside and still only counting three other cars in the parking lot, I went back in and said, "Now, I know you're fucking lying to me when you tell me you don't have any rooms. You have three options. One, you can politely ask me what type of room I'd like. Two, you can watch me sleep and hear me snore all night right here in this lobby, or three, you can call the law and explain to them why you are refusing to give me a room. Makes no fucking difference to me. I've been through a lot tonight, and either way, I know I'm sleeping well. Where that is, is up to you."

The young local hotel attendant looked at my clothes, which were hanging off my body and smelled like a rotting carcass. He made a wise choice when he said, "Okay. Sir, I apologize, we have rooms, but my computer is auditing itself. I don't know when it's going to be done. I'm so sorry I said we were booked."

The young local Comfort Inn employee, whose appearance was beyond shaken and who was probably just trying to follow company protocol, stared at me, waiting for my response. I figured the anger in my eyes said it all.

Finally, he gave in to his nutty new guest and said, "Okay, well, um, let me get your information and you can take Room 312. It's a king bed, um, smoking."

I leaned over the counter and looked the attendant in the eye. I didn't say anything, but the young man must have known what I was thinking.

Thanks, dude. Glad I'm not going to jail.

I took the room key and walked away. The attendant, stuttering, said, "Well, um, can I, um, let me get your information, Sir? Driver's license?"

As I got into the elevator, I yelled back, "Does it look like I have my driver's license on me? Don't worry, like I told you, the flood control engineers, company, insurance, whoever, will be taking care of everything. I give you my word. Thank you."

The elevator door closed. I walked down the hall to my room, opened the door, walked in, closed it, and broke down. I went from tough guy to baby in the time it took for the hotel room door to go from open to shut.

Why is this happening to me?

What have I done to deserve this?

When is it going to end?

I'm trying so hard! I'm trying so hard!

I ran a hot shower and didn't bother removing my clothes until I was convinced they had thoroughly rinsed. After all, I would have to wear them into the indefinite future.

Once I removed and rinsed my garments one more time, I placed them over the room heater. Then I went back into the tub and took the greatest shower I had ever taken. I shampooed my hair. I scrubbed my beard, which was growing back quickly from my second oral argument. I stayed in the shower for what had to have been nearly an hour, even sitting at one point at the bottom of the tub, thinking.

I have to get through this. Just a few more weeks.

# Chapter 36

God works His will in wondrous ways. It was Thursday, April 25, 2002, and the day after the detonation that rocked my life. I looked around. I was in a strange room with a strange odor and at a strange time of my life. It was 11:30 A.M. and I had no place to live. I didn't have any money, or clean underwear for that matter. What I did have, however, was the biggest test of my life in just five short days. Doctor McGhee's Contracts II exam was not going to wait for me to get my life back together—again.

I snuck out of the Comfort Inn and walked to the downtown Teen Center for the meeting Scooby told me about the night before. The Teen Center was in the blast zone, but I didn't notice any damage. As I entered, I looked around. Blugg, Scooby, and Barney Stiltner were the only people I recognized. I walked up to Blugg and asked him how he did with his wife.

"She done let me stay last night, but reckon I'm homeless like you tonight."

"Sorry, man. I hope these guys find us a place to live. I've got no funds for shelter and all the food I was planning on eating through the rest of the semester is probably floating around my apartment in that stench right about now."

"Well, let's see what these fellers say. They won't keep a good ol' boy down. I'll tell you what."

Deuce Shandi Insurance Company, the insurance company for the contractors responsible for the errant blast, had organized the community meeting. Finally, we got to hear what happened from the horse's mouth. An insurance adjuster said, "Folks, no need to be worried. Yesterday, we had an unfortunate minor incident. No one was seriously harmed, and there doesn't appear to be catastrophic damage. We realize that last night must have lasted forever for some of you. We just need you to do the things we say to do."

I heard that people had broken bones and the town resembled a war zone—who is this prick kidding? Minor incident, my ass.

The folks at the meeting were surprisingly patient with the adjuster. I wasn't. Neither was Blugg.

Blugg held his hand up high for a question. The adjuster called on him. Blugg asked, "Hey, you 'spect us to believe this shit ain't shit? Me and my buddy here ain't got no place to stay. What are ya'll going to do about that 'minor' problem?"

The squirmy adjuster replied, "One of my associates advised me of what occurred late last night. Mr. Carr and Mr. Burnside will be put up at the Anchor Inn. We have reason to believe that your problems were caused by the building, not something from the mishap, and perhaps not our insured's fault. It's our understanding that you all are law students and will be leaving Grundy in two weeks anyway, is that correct?"

I stood up and interrupted, "Well, actually it's a little over two weeks. And Blugg lives here. He'll need something more permanent. Do we have to stay at the Anchor? Can't we stay at the Comfort Inn? What about my things that have been destroyed?"

The adjuster looked at a clipboard and then looked up.

"The Anchor Inn is the only place we'll cover. As for your things, we'll probably declare them a total loss and you'll get fair market value for everything, that is, if we accept liability. You'll have to do an inventory and give us receipts for the things you've lost."

I was getting angry just thinking about the extra time the adjuster was asking me to take away from studying to do an inventory. I took a deep breath and said, "Well, I always walked to ASL. As I don't have two nickels to rub together, what do I do for food and gas for transportation from the Anchor? That's at least two miles away, in each direction."

"Well, you'll have to find the money somehow to pay for those items while we perform our investigation. Save all your receipts and send them to us when you go back home. And in case we deny your claims, you might want to contact your landlord. Please know our men are working hard."

Deny my claim? Is this guy fucking kidding me?

I didn't have the energy to fight.

"Okay, thank you."

Dick.

⚖

After the meeting, I went to ASL to pick up my Legal Process oral argument grade from my mailbox. I already knew I scored well on my motion for summary judgment and I had a good feeling after beating Portia. When I opened the envelope, I wasn't surprised to see a B+ on the argument, which gave me an overall B+ in the class.

Pumping my fist, I couldn't help but to blurt, "Fucking awesome!"

Because As were a rarity on ASL's low One L C+ grading curve, I was perfectly happy with the mark. It had to have been one of the best in the class. The B+ also boosted my spirits during that frustrating time. I had hoped that everything was falling into place.

⚖

My new home at the Anchor Inn looked like Elvis personally decorated it back in the 1970s and the room had never since been updated. It had a sagging full-sized bed, what looked to be one of the first color televisions ever sold, a dilapidated desk made out of particle wood, and a very musty bathroom. The walls were powder blue and covered with pink vertical stripes.

My new war room?

Considering the alternative of sleeping in the library, it wasn't bad. Once I got settled, I hung the damp, wrinkled clothes from my backpack over the balcony railings of the Anchor to dry. My raggedy-looking wardrobes actually improved the appearance of the rusting facade.

Once everything was unloaded and I was showered, I got in my jeep, prayed I wouldn't run out of gas, and drove to the post office, hoping to have received a credit card offer that day to live on until I returned home to Cleveland. I seemed to get those damn things in the mail all the time. I was relieved to discover that there was, indeed, an annoying damn credit card offer in the mail that day. I had exactly six cents in my bank account and nothing in my wallet.

After I drove to ASL to use the phone to activate the credit card, I got gas and then drove to Saint Joseph's to study. I began the day with nothing. I was going to end the day with shelter, my books, and a method to purchase food. That's all this vision quester needed.

After I arrived at Saint Joseph's, but before I began studying, I walked into the main church area and knelt in front of the hanging crucifix. I prayed my ass off.

I studied only for a short bit that night. I was tired and still a bit frazzled. After my mediocre study session, I went back to my apartment to retrieve some leftover beer. Some of it was floating in a cool rank puddle at the foot of my stove. I brought the beer back to the Anchor, rinsed off the cans, sat outside on the balcony, and tried to smell the roses.

Despite what the town looks like, my war is almost over.

The Friday before the Contracts II final exam, I woke up before my normal 5:30 A.M. buzzer. I wanted to finish summarizing Criminal Law and Property II in my outlines before Saturday. I chose to study at Saint Joseph's—I reeked badly and couldn't go to a laundry facility because I had no cash for quarters and no option on my credit card to get it. I was stuck with just a few outfits for the rest of my time in Grundy. And still no fucking underwear.

When I arrived at Saint Joseph's that day, I could somehow smell the spring air over the smell of myself. I studied all day outside in the sun, keeping my brain warm and motivated. As the sun was going down, I received a visitor. It was Sister Sofia with a hot plate of food and a warm smile. I apologized for being short with her the last few times that I saw her. She took the foil off the plate, handed me a fork, and simply said, "Apology accepted. Now eat."

While I ate, I told Sister Sofia about how I was praying and felt myself getting stronger. She smiled with delight. We also chatted about the blast and how ironic it was in light of the shootings. We then somehow got on the topic of the church's landscaping.

"Sister, how come the weeds are so tall on the hill along 460?"

"Honey, I can't get anyone to cut 'em. No one wants to do it."

"I'll do it. I feel indebted to you all for all you have done for me."

I spent all of Saturday, April 27, three days from my first exam, studying my Contracts II outline. After going through the outline for what had to have been the fifth time, I was still overwhelmed by the vast amount of material.

Shit. There are so many principles and defenses.

I knew I couldn't learn or stay motivated by reading over the same enormous outline for two days. I needed to come up with another method for memorization. I thought back to other ways my classmates studied for the fall semester exams and decided to borrow one of Tater's strategies. He wrote out mnemonics for each chapter and for each subheading.

That's how I'll beat this information into my brain!

After drudging through the entirety of the outline a few more times, I spent most of Saturday evening and Sunday creating mnemonics for Contracts II. "PRPPMT," or Pete Raps Performing Proud Mary Trucking helped me remember Policing the bargain, Remedies for breach, Performance and breach, Parol evidence, Mistake/impracticability/frustration and Third-party beneficiaries. Once I covered the main subjects, I even went as far as creating sub-sub-heading mnemonics for each case.

At the end of Sunday, I had six pages of mnemonics that I planned to memorize the next day. Being prepared for an exam was a damn good feeling—I had never felt it before. But I needed to be overly prepared, which is why I looked forward to the next day.

From the time I awoke that Monday morning, until 2:00 A.M., I finished memorizing all of my Contracts II mnemonics. The mnemonics, however, served only as reference points. I already had the knowledge that connected each point saved up in my mind from everything I did that semester to learn. Paying attention in class, taking notes, listening to audio lessons while walking around and driving to and from D.C., outlining on my down time, reviewing, and summarizing in my outlines was all going to pay off for me.

I knew Doctor McGhee's exam would be tricky. She was not above sneaking in a red herring from time to time to throw off her unsuspecting students. She would often disguise one red herring with two or three others. The evil Irishwoman formulated her questions like a leprechaun who gives false clues to the location of the pot of gold.

Before I ended the day, I went to the YMCA and had a great workout. While on the rowing machine, I took each stroke while reciting a different mnemonic. I solidified my memories with the rhythm of each pull.

Come on, 10 more strokes . . .

Material Breach Circumstances are . . .

"SAP CHIP."

Substantial benefit—One!

Adequately compensated—Two!

Partly performed—Three!

Certainty . . .

I ended that day pumped up. When I got back to the Anchor, I paced the room, thinking about how I couldn't wait to get to Doctor McGhee's exam. I couldn't wait to ace it.

Let's do this.

⚖

I awoke that crucial morning of April 30, 2002, and drove slowly to ASL. Despite all the memorization and all the summaries, outlines and law tapes, if I was to be successful, I knew the most important element to my success was something I couldn't study. Rule regurgitation would get me some points, but not enough for Dean's List.

When authoring my answers, I had to make it sound like I knew what I was talking about. My explanations had to be clear and justified. My conclusions had to be strong and confident. In order to sound like a lawyer, I had to think like a lawyer. I had to trust myself.

Once I arrived at ASL, everything became a blur. I remember parking my jeep across the Levisa River, saying one last prayer and thanking myself for not giving up. My time had come. I had overcome so much. I fought so hard.

Time to think like a lawyer, Jeremy.

⚖

Relief. Satisfaction. Retribution. These words best describe how I felt when I left ASL that day. During the exam, it had felt like my thoughts magically reverted themselves back to the Anchor Inn the night before when the answers to all of my questions popped into my head with ease—or when I was rowing, when the answers came into my head in rhythm with my strokes. After I secured the answers in my head, a supernatural power funneled them to my fingers, downloaded them into my pen, and inscribed them into my exam book.

I hadn't fallen for a single red herring. Unlike my drunken state in the fall semester, the only intoxicating feeling I had after the Contracts II final exam was the feeling of academic accomplishment. Although I experienced periodic flashes of assurance throughout the semester, I had never wholeheartedly pictured myself doing it. But with the confidence I took from my performance on that crucial exam, making Dean's List was no longer just a technically possible pipedream; it became a tangible reality.

When I got back to the Anchor, I called Hammer Mike. We talked about the blasting. He said, "Do you want me to drive Penelope down and get your shit?"

"Nah. There's nothing to get. It's all ruined."

With a chuckle to lighten the mood, Hammer Mike said, "Then do you need me to come down there and kick someone's ass?"

"No, dude, I'm okay. Actually, despite all this shit, I aced my first exam."

"Get the fuck out. My son aced a law school exam?"

"Unless my professor fucks me over, I think so."

"That's-a-my-boy! Yeeaah! Now finish strong!"

# Chapter 37

The Battle of the Crater was not General Ambrose Burnside's first taste of bad luck. Soon after he accepted his ultimate commission as leader of the entire Army of the Potomac, General Burnside was pressed into battle. President Lincoln was desperate for a big victory. It was mid-November 1862 and Lincoln needed political support for the Emancipation Proclamation, which Lincoln planned to sign on January 1, 1863.

Soon after President Lincoln pressured him to lead the Union Army, General Burnside addressed Lincoln's urgency by devising a battle plan focused in and around Fredericksburg, Virginia. Burnside believed that a swift victory at Fredericksburg would give the Union army a clear path to the Confederate capitol of Richmond and thus bring about the end of the Civil War. Similar to what would happen a few years later at Petersburg, Burnside theoretically had the United States on the brink of victory.

As fate would have it, though, Mother Nature flooded the Rappahannock River, which cut off the U.S. forces from Fredericksburg—destroying Burnside's hope for a quick assault. Bureaucratic bungling regarding who was to deliver pontoon bridges caused a delay of the crossing for weeks, eliminating the element of surprise. The longer the bridges took, the more time General Lee had to decipher Burnside's plan and organize his forces.

Because of the flooding, General Burnside wanted to re-group and devise another plan of attack. But President Lincoln pushed him to go forward with what became a watered-down assault. So on December 11, 1862, nearly a month after the original plan to cross, a reluctant General Burnside sent his engineers to lay out the late-arriving pontoon bridges across the swollen Rappahannock.

Burnside's forces eventually crossed the river, but General Lee had time to secure the high ground and direct his troops into far superior positions. The rebels not only used a stone wall as cover, but from the heights, they could see everything coming at them. But as the Union forces significantly outnumbered the Confederates, the U.S. still had a chance.

As the fighting intensified, Union Major General William B. Franklin, commander of one of Burnside's Three Grand Divisions, ignored Burnside's orders to support the main central attack on Marye's Heights. Without this critical support on the flank, Union soldiers led by "Fighting Joe" Hooker were slaughtered as they charged up the hill, unsupported. The Battle of Fredericksburg became one of the most bloody, one-sided battles in U.S. history.

After the battle, Lincoln wrote, "If there is a place worse than hell, I am in it."

If the Rappahannock River didn't flood, the Civil War may have ended years earlier than it did, and there would have been no Battle of the Crater. Thousands of lives, on both sides, would have been spared. Ambrose Burnside would have been an American hero.

But the flooding did happen. Just like it did to me 140 years later, in another part of Virginia, far from Fredericksburg.

# Chapter 38

On May 2, 2002, I was ready to flex my academic muscle and primed to finish exams strong. It was one day before the Criminal Law final exam, and the rain had been falling for hours. It was a heavy rain that never let up. The more it rained, the higher Slate Creek and the Levisa River rose. I thought little of it. I was too focused on making Dean's List.

I went to the YMCA at around 3:00 P.M. When I pulled in, I noticed that the water of Slate Creek was considerably up. To keep fresh and gear up for a long night, I leisurely shot a basketball around. As I was about to leave, the front desk lady stopped me. She said, "Jeremy, honey, I don't think you can go."

"Can't go, why?"

"Slate Creek is flooding the area. I'm actually getting ready to close up here."

"Oh, I'm sure it'll let up soon. Even if it doesn't, it's just a stream. We'll be fine, right?"

The front desk lady began closing up her logbooks and walked over to lock the entrance. She turned to me and patted my arm.

"Sweetheart, this is Grundy. A downpour like this is always big. Let's just hope and pray that it's about over."

Still, I thought little of the constant rain. I got into my jeep and drove towards the bridge that went over Slate Creek. In about the half hour that I shot baskets, Slate Creek's waters had shot up to a level covering the bridge leading to the YMCA, some two to three feet higher.

Because I had no time to be sidelined from my studies, I took a chance and drove my jeep over where I knew the bridge to be. I drove cautiously through the run, which fully covered my tires. I then sped towards ASL through the streaming creek that crested and was now covering the road. The overflow water finally subsided around Mountain Mission School, but I began to think something terrible was brewing. Things seemed eerie. I didn't see any other cars on the road.

The thick, pounding rain was not relenting. It was getting harder and uglier, much more forceful and unyielding than even the downpour the night of the blasting. I tried not to think about what was occurring outside, but it was impossible not to. I was worried that the Levisa River was flooding like Slate Creek on the other side of town. I believed there was a chance the Anchor Inn would get flooded because it sat on Levisa's banks.

This must be why they are blasting out the mountain behind my apartment—to stop this type of shit.

Come on, Jeremy. No distractions. Absolutely no distractions.

When I got to ASL, I walked into the library and sat down at my usual study carrel to review Criminal Law. From where I was sitting, I could hear the force of the rain getting even more powerful. I looked out the window and could not see any of the parked cars in the lot just adjacent to me.

What if the blasting caused damage to the flood control project, making the whole valley susceptible to waters higher than the historic '77 flood?

Shit! Come on, Jeremy. No distractions. Absolutely no distractions!

After about forty minutes of unsuccessful study marred by increasing anxiety, I walked into the main building to see what other people were doing. As soon as I walked into the Lion's Lounge, I bumped into Barney Stiltner, who looked beside himself and was in a hurry.

Franticly, he said, "Hey Cleveland. I can't get a hold of anyone here at the law school to ask them if we can use ASL as a shelter. Do you think the ASL bigwigs will mind?"

I replied, "I can try to track down Dean Lund. I think he lives around here. If not, a few professors live across the street. How bad is it?"

"The rivers and streams, son. They're all up beyond what we can handle. We're in for a time."

Even after the shootings and during the recent blasting debacle, Barney Stiltner remained cool as a cucumber. When he handled those tragedies, he was a professional lawman, just doing his job. He was anything but cool on that May 2002 day. Something was wrong. Something was very wrong.

"Okay, son. Listen, I'm going to help fetch the folks who are under water and bring them here. I need you to find someone at ASL to give me the official word."

A Three L was listening in on our conversation and had one of the tenured professor's cell phone numbers. The Three L volunteered to explain the situation to the ASL powers-that-be and get back in touch with Barney. Grundy's brave lawman wasn't done with me.

"Cleveland, people are in trouble out towards Hurley. We're going to have trouble getting to them. Many of the old timers living in trailers won't be able to get out. We've got to help them."

"We? As in you and me?"

Barney nodded.

I felt as I did when I heard Dennis Mensinger running through the halls of the library on January 16 screaming for help. I had an opportunity to do something, but just stood there. This time, however, I was faced with a direct request.

"Cleveland, I'm short on manpower and you look strong enough to help. You city folk can swim, right?"

Extreme selfishness was the feeling I experienced after Barney asked for my help. I wasn't as intimidated by the dangerous flooding as I was of my personal consequences if I went. If I went to help, I'd lose what I thought to be precious study time.

I cannot turn him down. I have to do this.

But I need more time preparing for tomorrow's exam. No distractions. Absolutely no distractions.

Fuck.

I looked at Barney, embarrassed as shit. I then hung my head low.

"Sorry, Chief Stiltner, I can't."

Barney looked back at me with disappointment and then disappeared to wherever it was his police cruiser was located. I let Barney Stiltner down. I let Buchanan County down. I hated that. I'd become a victim of my own obsession. To me, and at that time, I felt like I had no choice. I wanted to become a Two L—at any cost.

After leaving ASL, I drove to the Anchor to grab a few books and to see if Blugg wanted to go for dinner. I needed someone to tell me I made the right choice. The guilt associated with turning Barney down quickly dominated my thoughts.

I should've just gone.

Now I'm not going to be able to study because I'm just going to worry.

What if someone dies because of me and my studying?

When I got to the Anchor, Blugg was sitting on his bed with his door wide open, obviously waiting for someone other than me.

"Yo, Bluggster, is everything okay?"

"My trailer with my wife and youngins' is in Hurley. I tried to drive over there. Sum bitches won't let me through."

When I heard Blugg say, "won't let me through," I immediately was taken back twenty minutes.

Stupid.

"Well, Blugg, I hear Barney's on his way. I'll pray for you and your family. How about getting something to eat?"

"Thanks, City, but I ain't hungry."

I said nothing and tried not to get down on myself.

It's not my fault this flooding is going on, right? Surely, people will understand.

I walked out the door, got in my jeep and stared at myself in my rearview mirror. Stupid. I should be in Hurley.

I've made a big mistake.

Jeremy, you're a selfish asshole.

First you blow your opportunity in law school and now you put your head in the sand when faced with a meaningful duty—for what? To remedy your first mistake?

As I began to turn my ignition on, I heard rushing water close by. I jumped out and ran through the pitch-blackness and pouring rain towards the Levisa River. Before I knew it, I could hear the floodwaters getting closer and closer. I ran along the back of the Anchor. It didn't take long for me to realize that the Levisa River, like Slate Creek, had new banks and the Anchor Inn was only a few feet from being one of them.

Homeless.

Please, not again.

Folks in Hurley will be homeless.

Karma coming back at me.

⚖

The Criminal Law final exam was set to take place in a matter of hours and I needed to finish studying and remove myself from Buchanan County's growing floodwaters before they completely washed out my motivation. I went to a local Italian restaurant, sat in a booth and tried to regroup my emotions.

I need another strong performance tomorrow on this final exam. I've come this far and have sacrificed so much, including my dignity.

After taking a few hours to eat dinner, attempt to collect myself, and review my Criminal Law mnemonics, I drove back to the library. I pulled my Indians baseball cap over my eyes and snuck upstairs. I focused my first line of sight directly towards my normal study station. I looked around and knew that the library was too quiet for an early evening before a final exam. I walked around and soon made a peculiar realization.

The library is completely empty!

I thought that perhaps I was in a dream. I ran back down the stairs and checked the first floor again. There was no one. Not even a circulation desk clerk.

What's going on here?

I quickly walked over to the Lion's Lounge.

Certainly, someone is at ASL somewhere. The parking lot is nearly full.

I opened up the doors to the Lion's Lounge and saw what appeared to be displaced families spread out on the floor. There must have been twenty or thirty families occupying the crowded room. A cloud of grief and sadness again hovered over the lounge. The hopelessness in the eyes of ASL's newest residents brought me back to January 16.

Children were crying. Family heirlooms were kept close by. Families mourned the loss of their homes. Grundy had suffered another biblical-type tragedy. My selfishness nearly overtook my sympathy for those in front of me. I had to find out where all of the law students were. I wondered if they all went to volunteer and if I was the only able-body asshole still safe at the school. I looked in my mailbox for answers and found them.

Fuck.

There was a memo from Dean Lund indicating that ASL had cancelled final exams the next day because of the flooding. Many students lived in the hardest hit area of Buchanan County, Hurley, and the floodwaters of Slate Creek prevented travel from that side of the county.

What that meant to me was that I would have my last three final exams all during the next week. I had planned for two exams that week and was ready for the Criminal Law final exam for the next day. At that moment, all I could think was that it really fucked up my plan.

I tore up the piece of paper. Rage took over.

What the fuck? I'm ready now!

Each day was planned out! Now I have to rearrange everything again!

I stormed out of the Lion's Lounge, ignoring a request from a little boy for me to retrieve a toy truck he zoomed under one of the couches.

Why do these things keep happening to me?

It's as if God sees me overcome one obstacle and then pushes me in to another!

If there is a place worse than hell, I am in it.

I immediately got in my jeep and drove to the nearest non-flooded gas station and charged a large amount of beer. I was so upset, I began drinking the beer the second I pulled off. I then drove straight to the Anchor Inn and invited myself into Blugg's room, which door was still open. By the time I arrived, I had already chugged three beers. I opened a fourth and tossed one over to Blugg.

"Blugg, this is bullshit. Did you hear about finals? Don't you think this is fucked up?"

Blugg opened the beer slowly and said, "No, but finals ain't on the top of my list of thangs to be worryin' 'bout raught now. I'm sattin' right hair and waitin' for that damn phone to rang. Once again, I'm waitin' for someone to tell me that my old lady and youngins' are okay."

"Well, ASL's Lion's Lounge is full, but I didn't see anyone that matches the description you gave me of your family."

Blugg spit some tobacco juice in a plastic Mountain Dew bottle then said, "I don't 'spect they're there or I reckon they wudda called the Anchor."

"Dude, the Criminal Law final is cancelled tomorrow. That means we have three fucking finals next week, three! How do they expect us to handle that?"

"Whoa, City Boy. Chill out, man. You've got to remamber, ev-rie sum bitch in our class has to take three finals in five days. Simmer it on down now."

"I can't! What the fuck, Blugg? Within the last week, we've had to rearrange our lives because of the blasting, and now this? It's not fucking fair!"

Blugg took out his dip and had a sip of his beer. He said, "Well, again, you have to remamber that you ain't the only feller going through this shit. I mean, not to make you fil sorry for me, but, shit, I ain't got no place to live, neither. And shit, that's not to mantion the fact that I don't know anythang about my family's safety."

"But if you only knew that my grades . . ."

"Thank about it, City. Thank about it and drank that beer and shut the hell up."

# Chapter 39

When I woke up late that Friday morning, the original day of the Criminal Law final exam, things weren't that bad, after all. I was no longer consumed by fury and although I cringed thinking about having three more days to ponder Criminal Law, I felt better knowing that my classmates were probably frustrated as well. Things always seem better in the morning.

After spending the day peacefully studying at Saint Joseph's, I returned to the Anchor, hoping to catch my second wind. I stopped by Blugg's room to see how he was doing. I knocked on his door and a woman I suspected to be his estranged wife answered in just a NASCAR tee shirt.

I asked her, "Can Blugg come out to play?"

The skinny, attractive woman smiled and directed Blugg to the door. When he arrived, he had two kids hanging over his neck and back. I smiled and asked, "Hey Blugg, glad to see everything's okay. Do you want to go with me to ASL and study?"

"Sorry, City Boy. Raught now there are more 'portant thangs for me to do."

"I see that," I said. "Enjoy yourself, but don't forget that you need to study."

"Will do, buddy. Jus' as long as you don't firget that you need to enjoy yirself and stop bein' a damn stick in the mud."

I left the Anchor and drove to ASL with no plans to enjoy myself that night or any other night for the rest of my time in Grundy. When I pulled into ASL's parking lot, I noticed that the Lion's Lounge was more congested. There were news vans in the parking lot. I remembered at least two of the same news vans from January 16. Before walking into the library, I stopped and asked one of the reporters how things were. A young lady with forty pounds of make-up on her face was quick with her response.

"Hurley just up Slate Creek looks like a hurricane hit it. Totally devastated. People are dead. Many of the ones who aren't, wish they were. Care to comment?"

I entered the library and looked around. It was again empty.

Why would this place be full? My classmates are doing what Blugg is doing.

My classmates are trying to enjoy themselves before our next week of hell.

I sat down at a cubicle. I sat and stared.

Who am I kidding? I'm not getting anything done tonight.

I quickly left ASL and went to Saint Joseph's to pray. When I opened the door to the church section of the building, I saw Sister Sofia kneeling with her rosary in hand.

I said, "Sister Sofia? Sorry to interrupt. Is everything okay?"

Sister Sofia opened her eyes, turned and said, "Jeremy, so much has already happened this year. Do you remember that we talked about flooding in February?"

"Yes. How can I forget? I thought about it until I thought the flooding was gone from my soul."

Sister Sofia reached for the Bible and opened it to a marked reading. She said, "Do you remember me reading you, 'I sink deep in mire where there is no standing; I am come into deep waters, where the floods overflow me?' "

"Yes. That was at a point where I felt myself sinking in some pretty deep mire."

Rubbing her eyes, Sister Sofia said, "Well, I pray for those literally being flooded now in Buchanan County. Father Joe and I were down there today volunteering. We would volunteer more, but there didn't seem to be much more we could have done with the water still high. What a tragedy. God help them."

I didn't know what to say. I felt terrible that I rejected Barney's call for my help to go into the dangerous areas caused by the flooding. There was only one thing I could do about it at that moment. I picked up a rosary and knelt down next to the sorrowful Sister. I prayed the rosary with her until we completed all of the Mysteries.

When Sister Sofia got up to leave, she said, "Remember, Jeremy, He hears your struggle. If you struggle again, you know who to talk to."

"I know. It's just much easier talking to someone you can see and who talks back. Like you, for example."

Sister Sofia smiled and said, "He talks back. You just have to listen."

"I do listen . . ."

"No, Jeremy, listen with your heart, not your ears."

I woke up on Saturday, May 4, 2002, rejuvenated. After a few prayers, I felt empowered and ready to rock. I spent that Saturday finishing my Civil Procedure II mnemonics. I also began to formulate some for Property II. I was very efficient that day. Again, I felt my soul becoming closer and closer to discovering who I was and where I was in the circle of life.

When I awoke that Sunday morning, I immediately began reading over my Criminal Law outline. I read it and read it and read it. I wrote out my mnemonics several times throughout the morning. I found that each time I thought I needed to memorize something else, I already knew it. While praying about the exam during Mass, I realized that I knew all I was going to know about Criminal Law.

It was Monday, May 6, 2002, and finally time for the Criminal Law final exam. When I walked into ASL, which had been cleared of its refuges with the help of the Red Cross, I stood in front of the fall semester Dean's List posting, which still hung by the mailroom. I briefly closed my eyes and pictured it being fall 2002 with my name gracing the spring semester Dean's List posting.

I just have to survive this week. Then it's out of my hands.

When I charged into the exam room, I held nothing back. I answered the questions as fast as I could, channeling my anger at the rescheduling. Despite my haste, however, I was still able to use my imagination to think like a lawyer.

Although I had some aspirations of becoming a criminal defense lawyer, my main interest in Criminal Law came from following Peter O's capital murder case. For the many questions about Mens Rea, or mental state, my ability to easily answer those questions came from my efforts to fully understand Peter O's pending legal mental-capacity challenges. One rumor circulating ASL was that Peter O was saying that he didn't mean to kill anyone in the Lion's Lounge.

In my answer to one question about whether a baseball player acted with a criminal intent when he flung his bat into a crowd in frustration after striking out,

I compared the batter with a shooter who fires bullets into a crowd. Like the shooter, who may not have actually intended to kill anyone, the hitter knew, or should have known, someone would be harmed shortly before he released his bat. I argued that such reckless intent is enough for a conviction.

After I turned in my answer booklet, I exited the room and walked directly back to the Dean's List posting. I just wanted to see it again before my final preparations for the Property and Civil Procedure exams. Seeing it once more made me realize that my whining and complaining about my life were not going to help me achieve my impossible feat. In order to finish strong, I had to stay 48th-Street tough.

# Chapter 40

Rejuvenated after the Criminal Law exam, I finally took time to cut the brush along the dangerously steep hill at Saint Joseph's that ran parallel to U.S. Route 460. I had to fetch my waterlogged baseball cleats from my apartment in order to keep my footing, or I could have easily fallen onto the road and been splattered by an oncoming coal truck. It was a hot day so I placed my hair in a ponytail, wore only a stale pair of shorts, and didn't bother with a shirt.

It took a few hours to complete. When I was done, I went back to the Anchor Inn, covered in diced green weeds. I decided to wait to shower until after reviewing my Civil Procedure II outline a few times. I reviewed on my bed, drifting in and out of sleep.

Before I fell asleep for the night, I thought about how we only had one day of studying in between each final exam, instead of the two days that were originally scheduled before the flooding occurred. But I finally realized that the revised final exam schedule actually worked in my favor. When my classmates had thought they'd have two days in between finals, some of them likely procrastinated with their outlines. Mine were done. My other classmates in study groups were probably struggling to find time to meet. I didn't rely on anyone else to have that problem.

May 7th: one day before I became one final away from becoming either a Two L or a law school flunky. It was hard for me to stay motivated when I knew I was a few short days from being home with my family, hanging with my friends, and sitting at Jacobs Field enjoying life while taking in a Cleveland Indians baseball game. A few short days away from being just a dude again.

My mnemonics for Civil Procedure II consisted only of chapter headings and sub-headings. I didn't go into detail with sub-sub-headings and cases because I wanted to concentrate on learning the rules. I studied the packet I had copied of the Federal Rules of Civil Procedure so much, and had taken so many notes, that I ran out of room to write.

I was long past looking at my Civil Procedure outline and focused on memorizing the boring subject's many intricacies. I limited myself to memorizing the rule, where the rule came from and how I thought Dickey would use that rule to try to make me fail. But I wasn't going to fail his exam—unless something else happened.

As May 7 progressed, the day grew hotter and hotter. I began to feel a strange sensation throughout my body. It felt like little micro-people were running around my skin, lighting little fires. To prevent the resulting anxiety from becoming a complete nightmare, I tried to picture Dickey's face. I kept telling myself that he was the one who should feel anxiety—someone he believed didn't belong in law school was going to ace his exam.

At 6:30 P.M., while eating dinner, I noticed itchy sores raising from my skin all over my body. I looked at my hands. I looked at my arms. Beady red blisters were appearing everywhere. They were already in my ears, in between my fingers, and on my face. It was destined to be the worst case of poison ivy I'd ever experienced.

When I awoke that morning of Dickey's exam, I opened my motel door and took a deep breath. It was a nice, atypically sunny Grundy day. The sun was directly overhead, which allowed its rays to be free from the shadows of Grundy's towering mountains. I gathered my things and drove to the library, itching and scratching the whole way there. The condition of my skin was worsening.

I saw Blugg shortly before the exam. He looked at me and said, "Hey City, you get them hives when you get stressed?"

"No, Blugg. I wish that's what this was."

Blugg shook his head and smiled. "Well, I reckon you must be the unluckiest feller I ever done met."

I changed the subject and asked Blugg about his family. He told me that he was allowed back home and that his wife finally sounded supportive of his ambitions to become a lawyer. Blugg also told me that since his family's trailer was destroyed in the flood, he was trying to get his insurance company to quickly evaluate his losses so he could get payment and start a new life. A new life was what I was about to have myself.

"Blugg, when these finals are over, I, too, will have a fresh new start. I owe a lot of my sanity these last few weeks to you. Thanks, brother."

I reached out my hand for Blugg to shake it. He smiled and pulled me in for a hug. He didn't care that I looked like a leper. Bluggton Wayne Carr was an Appalachian One L through and through. I couldn't wait to see him as an attorney and it seemed the feeling was mutual.

"City Boy, you've did what no one else would've did. When ever-one else would've quit, you stuck it out. Now go into this exam and show Dickey's ornery ass who the hell you are and why the hell you came to Grundy, Virginia."

And I did just that. That day, I took Dickey's Civil Procedure II final exam with same vital force I summoned when I lost all that weight for wrestling, and that I exercised for the majority of my spring semester of law school. There were a few questions straight from his examples, several red herrings, questions not covered in my mnemonics, but all of which I was ready for. Blugg's little pep talk helped me block out what was occurring with my body and made me want to kick the Civil Procedure exam's ass.

Just as I did for the Criminal Law final exam, I cruised from question-to-question, knowing every answer. I did stumble in answering some of the questions, which I attributed to the poison ivy that began to itch relentlessly halfway through the exam. But I regrouped and somehow found a way to remain focused.

It was obvious that Dickey singled me out with the last question, which involved the proper venue of a law-abiding NRA member who wanted to challenge a state gun-control statute. Although tempted to make a snide remark in my answer, I realized that if I did that, Dickey would discover it was me and he would thereupon doom me. Even if he didn't sniff me out from ASL's anonymous grading system, I didn't want to take any chances. Too much was at stake. So I stayed cool, spotted the issue, and answered the question.

I was done with Dickey Eisen.

# Chapter 41

I had one step left to take from the mire of hate, insignificance, and depression that I'd been sinking in all semester. One step until I won my inner war and placed myself in a good position to make Dean's List. But three words ruled my body: obnoxious, overwhelming, and oozing. The poison ivy that I tried my best to ignore became too unbearable.

After the Civil Procedure II exam was over, I tried not to think about what was occurring, but I couldn't help it. I returned to the Anchor Inn and packed everything that didn't have to do with Property II in preparation for my trip home. I packed up my clothes, which had been somewhat rinsed by the rainwater on the balcony from the day of the flooding. They had finally dried.

I remained in the room with my one set of clothes, some free motel soap, my Property II outline and mnemonics, and my misery. I had to take action. The itching was too much.

I can't fucking take it anymore!

So I gave in. I took off my clothes, went in the shower, stood under piping hot water and vigorously scratched every area of infestation. As I raked my fingernails into my skin, trying to satisfy every unending itch, a mixture of blood, pus, and indescribable seepage spread everywhere from the exploded blisters. When I was done, I stood naked in the mirror above the motel room desk to assess the damage.

I said to myself, "Holy fucking shit."

My body's reaction to the poison ivy attacked my ears, spread to my eyes, trekked down my neck, radiated to my arms, settled in the crevices of my fingers, reversed to my stomach, around to my back, down the ridge of my butt and continued along my legs, covering each one like spandex onto my feet and with no mercy, attacked my toes. It didn't take me long to figure out where I exposed myself to the plant. I found it ironic that the place I retreated to escape distraction much of that semester was the same place where I received perhaps my biggest one.

I was able to bandage most of the wounds with towels from the Anchor, held on with duct tape I retrieved from the front desk that I said I needed to replace the old duct tape holding together the motel-room dresser. I covered myself like a mummy but couldn't find a way to stop the oozing from coming out of the corners of my eyes. The ooze didn't stop, no matter how long I'd apply pressure.

Bandaged and battered, I still needed to move on and somehow prepare for the Property II final exam. I took several antihistamines to help me resist the urge to scratch. I drove to the library a complete mess.

When I arrived at ASL, it was around 2:00 P.M. I looked around at all of my classmates studying diligently. They were looking back at me like I had just walked out of a burn unit. My classmates whispered when I was out of sight. I heard things like:

"What happened to him now?"

"He looks like an alien."

"It has to be some type of disgusting disease!"

I set my books down on my study carrel tabletop, turned on the desk lamp, and opened my books. I couldn't believe what was happening. On the other hand, maybe I wasn't that surprised after everything that had happened to me that semester. I was in enough pain that any normal person would have checked in at a hospital. I didn't have the money and I sure as hell didn't have the time.

*Seriously, is this really happening?*

*Be tough. 48th-Street alley cat.*

I shook my head and grimaced in disbelief. For two hours, I thought more and more about what had occurred to me that semester and less and less about the Property II exam. Dejected, in agonizing pain and in utter disappointment of what kept occurring to me, I left the library and drove back to the Anchor Inn. If I weren't trying to be tough, I probably would have suffered an emotional meltdown.

When I got to the Anchor, I pulled out my outline. I began reviewing it. Again, I couldn't concentrate. I pulled my mnemonic formulas out of my bag. I attempted to recite them to no avail. I was in a constant state of frustration at a time when I needed to be in a deep state of focus. I needed to brush away the thoughts of what was occurring just as I did the weeks prior with the blasting and the flooding. But I couldn't. The agony was too much. So I decided to go to the woods.

Throughout my journey that semester, I sometimes believed that I had found my totem, or symbol communicating my vision in the circle of life. Each time I thought this, it turned out that I was wrong and was merely attempting to force a vision. For examplc, my discussion with Dennis in the Lion's Lounge on January 16 was not brought about by the carved wooden lions in the Lion's Lounge—it was just a discussion. The damsel in the silver gown who inspired my position on guns was just an apparition. My feeling of Abraham Lincoln directing me to march on Richmond was only fantasy.

I took the rest of that day off and drove to Breaks Interstate Park. I was going to take off my makeshift bandaging and allow the wind from the valley to sooth my wounds. "The Breaks," as first dubbed by Daniel Boone as he searched for a new path into Kentucky, is a forest area on the border of Virginia and Kentucky. It's a beautiful place known for its breathtaking gorge, a valley so big it's nicknamed the "Grand Canyon of the South." During the fall semester, I would often go there to mountain bike or clear my head. Lois and I sometimes went there to make love. We found a spot on a freestanding rock face that overlooked the entire valley. It felt like you were on top of the world.

Once I climbed to my spot, I took off the duct-taped towels. They had already fused to my wounds in some areas. I allowed the breeze to appease my pain and breathed in the cool spring air. I took a few more anti-itch pills and watched the birds soar effortlessly through the valley. Deer were drinking from the waters of the creek at the bottom. I sat and stared at the awesomeness that surrounded me. The world wasn't such a bad place, after all.

My spot perched overlooking the gorge could very well have been the special spot of famous miner John Swift, who buried a vast treasure near a "peculiar rock" in 1769. My spot was likely once occupied by Shawnee and Cherokee Indian hunters. Most significantly to me, my spot may very well have been the same spot that Shawnee and Cherokee vision questers experienced their visions.

The valley was preparing to sleep as the orange sun began its descent behind the welcoming mountains. I sat on the ground, with my feet crossed and my back against a tree. The multiple pills I chugged down to help with the itch made me very sleepy. The relaxing air calmed my senses even more and I drifted off.

After what seemed like several hours of sleep, I awoke. For some reason, I felt myself repeating, "Do not be afraid. Do not be satisfied," as if these words had been implanted in my mind during my slumber.

Throughout the semester, I had created many enemies. But Hammer Mike was right about the one I overlooked, my worst enemy: Fear.

Fear of failure. Fear of trying. Fear of uncertainty.

At about the time I realized what the words repeating in my head meant, I heard a primal call coming from above. I looked up and saw an eagle soaring over the mountains.

My totem.

# Chapter 42

It was my final evening in Virginia. When I got back to the Anchor, I studied my mnemonics for Property II over and over. I thought of that time as my opportunity to allow my experience that semester to come full circle. I had started that semester afraid and academically insignificant, like Peter O. I was finishing strong and knowledgeable, like someone Dean Sutin and Professor Blackwell wanted Peter O to be, someone like Angela Dales.

Although spiritually sharp, I was physically and mentally drained. But I just needed to muster enough stored-up vigor to finish strong. I was out of the mire. I was the champion of my Appalachian War. I had found my totem. I just needed to run with my head up towards the finish line of academic accomplishment.

When I rowed, my coach would always encourage me and my fellow oarsmen to release everything we had in the last 250 meters of a 2,000-meter crew race. He instructed us to leave all of our energy on the water. Just like in rowing, where I'd pour all of my leftover strength into those last 250 meters and take with me nothing from the water, I studied all of that final night in Grundy until my mind hurt. I wanted to use all of my leftover brainpower on that last exam.

So when I arrived at ASL that morning to take the Property II exam, I did just that.

In the last 250 meters of a rowing race, there are typically around 20 remaining strokes. On the Property II final exam, there were 20 questions. I treated the completion of each question like a final stroke at the end of a race.

When I finished that final question of that last exam, I took a deep breath. I didn't look to my left and I didn't look to my right. I looked within.

# Chapter 43

On May 15, 2002, just five days after the Property II final exam, one final disaster hit: a fire ripped through downtown Grundy. The blaze ironically destroyed much of what the blasting and flooding could not. I was physically home in Cleveland when it happened, but mentally, I hadn't left. As the Grundy tragedies of 2002 had become so intertwined with my recent rite of passage, I shed my last tear of that semester. I was trying to move on.

Soon after I returned home, I got a job as an usher with the Cleveland Indians and began work as an intern in the Cuyahoga County Prosecutor's Office. I was doing my best to use what I learned in Grundy to personally heal and become human again. I had faith that if I had failed, God had a good plan for me. My spring semester grade report no longer held ultimate importance in my life. But it was a significant symbol of things to come.

On June 11, 2002, I was checking my messages to see if there was any more feedback from the *ASL Memorial 5k*. When I accessed my ASL email account, I saw a message from Dean Lund. My eyes were drawn directly to the subject line.

| jburnside@mail.a | INBOX | |
|---|---|---|

| | |
|---|---|
| To: | jmb@asl.edu |
| Subject: | dean's list |
| From: | Paul Lund <plund@asl.edu> |

Jeremy:

Congratulations! Your academic performance for the Spring 2002 semester placed you in the top 25% of your class for that semester, and as a result you will named to the Dean's List for the Spring 2002 semester.

Paul E. Lund

Interim Dean and Associate Professor

I tried not to get too excited. After all, I felt that even if I made the bottom of Dean's List, it might not have pulled my grade up enough to a 2.0. I was still figuring top 10% is where I needed to be. I would have to wait for my full grade report. I thought about how bad it would suck if I became the only student in law school history to make spring Dean's List, but still fail out."

For two more days, I waited patiently. Then it came, restoring my sanity. I opened–

**Grade Report Form**

**Spring 2002**

**Burnside, Jeremy M.**

| Course | Course Description | Grade | Class Grade | Credits Attempted | Credits Received | Quality Points |
|---|---|---|---|---|---|---|
| LAW0103 | Contracts II | A | | 3.00 | 3.00 | 12.00 |
| LAW0105 | Property II | C- | | 3.00 | 3.00 | 5.01 |
| LAW0107 | Criminal Law | B- | | 3.00 | 3.00 | 8.01 |
| LAW0113 | Civil Procedure II | B- | | 3.00 | 3.00 | 8.01 |
| LAW0199 | Legal Process II | B+ | | 3.00 | 3.00 | 9.99 |
| | | | TOTALS | 15.00 | 15.00 | 43.02 |

Semester GPA 2.87

Cumulative GPA 2.30

Registrar

Despite having a good feeling about exams, I still couldn't believe what I saw. I thought maybe ASL had my name mixed up with another Jeremy in the class, who was very intelligent and whose last name was near mine.

Glorious! I was not only a Two L, but my score was near the top of my One L class! As I held the liberating paper in one hand, I pointed to the air with the other, like I had just crossed the finish line in first place of a grueling marathon.

It was party time. I did it! I was a Two L!

I was going to become a lawyer!

During that jubilant summer, I thought a lot about Peter O. At that time, he was still mounting his defense against the charges of murder and was still facing

Virginia's electric chair. I thought about how Peter O could have done what I did and how I could have done what he did. He could have been a Two L and I could have given in to my desperation and failure. We once were Appalachian One Ls together, but Peter O never found his place in the circle—I did—and as a result, I succeeded despite the odds against me.

I also thought a lot about what Dennis had originally said about how it would be impossible for me to get off probation. Throughout my One L spring semester at ASL, I learned that there is only one thing in life that makes something impossible: not being able to summon the optimism for a further attempt. But I also learned that so as long as we set ourselves on a path to achieve what others only speculate as unattainable, do we create a mystical moment in time that authenticates the committed venture as alternatively real, or just possible. This convoluted explanation can be simply defined as faith—the one miracle God intended that we create ourselves.

It was faith that I discovered on my own at The Breaks. It was what I had been looking for all along. My vision wasn't so much a moment of spiritual clarity as it was an awakening of something that I had carried with me my entire life. Through their own life tribulations and lessons, which I had failed to appreciate, my parents had already given me the formula to be successful. My dad taught me not to be afraid and my mother showed me it was okay to simply believe. I just had to go dark place inside of myself and struggle to put it all together.

In the end, I realized that my unlikely triumphs from my spring semester of my One L year of law school boiled down to two simple actions: when my fear emanating from reason and logic appeared right, I looked to my left. When tragedies struck and the fear magnified, I looked up.

# Epilogue

**Sunday, March 29, 2015.**

**12:15 P.M.**

I just returned home from Mass with this idea to describe my One L epilogue. I figured a journal entry nearly thirteen years from the day my story began would be appropriate. If you've read the whole book, you may have some questions about what has happened since that day I received my first semester grade report and almost went home to become a truck driver.

Not too much has changed about who I am since that dark semester when I decided that I needed to make my life worse in order for it to get better. I still wear Chuck Taylors and heavy metal tee shirts. I also plan on going to see Judas Priest in concert this summer. I still go to Mass and continue to grow in my faith. I still drink beer and still love my Cleveland Browns. But even as I stay the same, life itself has gone on.

Most significantly to my story, Hammer Mike died of lung cancer a few years ago at the age of 51. Throughout the rest of my time in law school, Hammer Mike continued to be my cool voice of reason. His advice usually consisted of his hillbilly one-line words of wisdom as well as his universal short phrases such as, "Fuck that," or, "Tell 'em to kiss your ever-livin' ass," which I sometimes catch myself repeating. It took me nearly a year after law school to break down and use a cell phone, but when I did, it was worth it because I got to talk to my dad several times a day. If it wasn't for him, I can't imagine what this epilogue would say.

In 2004, I took the Hillbilly Highway home to Cleveland and passed the Ohio bar exam on my first attempt. After being sworn in as an attorney, a fellow KISS fan hired and mentored me in the area of personal injury law. For five great years, I lived the dream I envisioned during law school. I spent quality time with my dad and his black Chihuahua named Harley, represented a few of the patrons at Henry's Bar, and reestablished my relationships with the rest of my family. I did all of this while trying cases to juries and learning what it takes to be a successful lawyer.

My passion regarding the proliferation of guns has not waned, but continues to develop. I still believe that disturbed and violent people such as Peter O should not be able to go to a swap meet and easily walk away with a semiautomatic equalizer. Ironically enough, Virginia Tech, which is located not far away from Grundy and just east on U.S. Route 460, had its own Peter O-type killer visit its campus in 2007. I remember the Virginia Tech killings well, as the massacre occurred just days after I returned from that area after participating in the fifth Annual *ASL Memorial 5k*.

Despite my continued hope that gun violence might one day decline, my attitude towards gun "rights" has changed a bit. I no longer believe that totally eliminating guns from everyone is the answer. And don't worry—I'm no longer interested in "taking your guns"—but if I could prevent you from being able to buy an assault rifle or legally restrict where and how your handgun is kept in relation to children, I would. I would also make everyone subject themselves to a background check, required training and testing—similar to what you would do when trying to obtain a driver's license. To the "good guys with guns": what's the big whoop with that?

But I don't think the people I disagree with about gun "rights" have anything to worry about when it comes to what the judiciary will continue to say is constitutional. With the United States Supreme Court essentially proclaiming that every American is part of a state militia to justify the pro-gun 2008 *District of Columbia v. Heller* decision, it's going to take at least a few more generations of mass shootings before the Court decides to revisit and redefine the issue.

To do my part, I served on the board of trustees for the Ohio Coalition Against Gun Violence and have engaged in television and university debates with various pro-everyone-should-carry-gun groups. Ultimately, however, it is our legislators who need to grow a collective backbone and stand up to the NRA. That will start once the voters have seen enough gun violence and start to pose a threat to NRA-backed reelection campaigns.

The Appalachian School of Law is strong and continues to evolve. If I would have waited just one year to apply to ASL, I wouldn't have gotten in, as required LSAT scores heighten every year. While only provisionally accredited when I attended in 2001–2004, ASL became fully accredited by the American Bar Association in 2006. When I got the announcement of ASL's accreditation in the mail, I almost started to cry. I did cry when I discovered that ASL's 2008 bar passage rate was among Virginia's highest. And with that, the dream of Dean Sutin, Professor Blackwell, and Angela Dales officially came true.

⚖

A few years ago, Grundy's Flood Control Project became complete, right on time. They got that mountain across from my old apartment blasted out to help the Levisa's flow and to make way for much needed flat land. Now there are no cute little shops, pretty brick roads, and primped trees lining quaint walkways. Most townsfolk are glad about that. They are glad because they've received what they believe to be greater—the world's first three-story WalMart Supercenter—complete with 230 jobs the town so desperately needed. New restaurants are soon to follow, which will surely bring new hope to the frequently devastated community.

Most of my classmates went on to bright careers in the law. Some of them married within the class and a few have since passed away. One of my good friends, and former ASL classmate, Justin Marlowe, helped me become human again during my Two L and Three L years. We went rock climbing and mountain biking at The Breaks and partied together. Marlowe and I are currently in the process of planning our annual trek back to Grundy for the 2016 *ASL Memorial 5k*, which is still going strong.

About five or six years ago at the race, I asked Police Chief Barney Stiltner (he was still directing traffic) if he remembered when he asked me to help him save folks trapped during the flood in Hurley. Barney didn't recall the conversation and I was glad he didn't, as I am still embarrassed by my refusal to this day.

In 2009, my life journey took me to Portsmouth, Ohio, a small river town located on the Ohio River. I chose to move back to Appalachia because I had an opportunity to practice law on my own without all of the competition that currently overwhelms the Cleveland personal injury market. That, and a big part of me missed the slower way of life I embraced in Grundy and West Virginia.

Portsmouth is famous for being the home of Branch Rickey, the baseball icon who signed Jackie Robinson. It is also the former home of the Detroit Lions, which were called the Portsmouth Spartans in the early 1930s. It would be a cool place for you to visit—especially if you like beer—as we are home to Ohio's oldest brewery.

In just five and half years here in Portsmouth, I've tried a high-profile aggravated murder case, built a very successful personal injury and wrongful death practice, met and married the love of my life, Madelyn Rose, and had a beautiful baby girl we named Maura. We recently found out that we have another baby on the way. If it's a boy, Maddie and I plan to name him Michael, my little "Hammer," no doubt.

Maddie is a real estate broker and we share office space in an old church we recently bought and have repurposed. The old worship area is a mock courtroom that we allow for mock trial use and for trial preparation and practice with clients. I believe that my new law office is only one of a handful of law buildings in the country to be located in an old church. I bought it to project strength and hope to my clients—two things often preferable to the money they are entitled to.

In the last three years, I've battled for the little guy in several cases no one else wanted. And I was able to earn successful verdicts and other resolutions. Not to sound like a cheesy lawyer commercial, but I really do take my clients' struggles personally. Whether it's bringing justice against a lazy nursing home, for a family who lost a loved one, or for a brain-injury client who seems to have lost everything, I feel good about what I do.

As I age, I'll never forget where I came from, both geographically and spiritually. I've proudly used that fighting spirit I found in my Appalachian War and One L vision quest to advance the rights of victims against the interests of big, greedy insurance companies. I can only hope that one day people will see tort "deform" as nothing more than big money's tool to hack away at the Seventh Amendment and the rights of the average citizen to get his or her case in front of a jury.

Pope John Paul II frequently said, "Do not be afraid." I found out back then—and still realize now—that those words are the words that I continually need to accept and build upon. I still have fear, but that fear no longer has that doomsday effect as it did in law school. I now know that it is okay to lower my net into deep waters for a catch, or, as the Polish Pope undoubtedly meant, it's okay to have faith. It took me over ten years of writing and editing this book to realize that my story was ultimately about my struggle to simply believe—in myself and in the hopeful revelation that everything will somehow be okay.

⚖

I didn't write this book to make money and don't want my classmates to think that I have exploited my own experience that fateful semester for personal gain. And just because I chose to write about my experience, doesn't make mine the worst. I initially started writing this book to ward off depression and since decided to publish it to memorialize the struggles and resulting lessons of my former self, whom I'd hate to be today. And who knows, maybe that sorry overachieving dreamer's story will somehow help someone.

I never meant this book to be a crime story and consider what eventually happened to Peter O mostly irrelevant to my story. Nevertheless, I am not naive to the prospect that you still want to know what happened to my one-time law-school classmate.

Peter O, like me, is also practicing law. He is currently residing near Grundy, in Pound, Virginia. Like me, he practices law with a number. My Ohio bar number is 0077980. His number is 1090193. Like me, who will take a medical malpractice case if the right circumstances permit, Peter O has recently filed a lawsuit against a doctor for failing to provide proper medical treatment. Also like me, Peter O represented someone who, in 2007, claimed injuries allegedly resulting in an ear condition called tinnitus. Peter O, like me, could perhaps argue that he is living his dream, practicing law.

Peter Odion-Iyore Odighizuwa is currently an inmate at Red Onion State Prison where he is living out his several life sentences in the same manner he lived in the outside world. He is filing lawsuits on behalf of himself, hoping some judge will eventually coddle him as many of us did during the 2001–2002 school year. In 2004, during my final semester of law school, and the year in which Peter O should have been taking the bar exam, Judge Johnson's replacement sentenced him to several life sentences in exchange for a controversial plea bargain to save his life. Not all of the victims wanted him to live and although I'm against the death penalty, I can't say I blame them.

During Peter O's sentencing hearing, Marlowe and I found seats in the back of the overflowing Buchanan County courtroom, next to a sweaty newspaperman. Several witnesses were there to provide victim impact statements. Everyone was buzzing over what they thought the victims were going to say.

Little did I know that a surprising witness would again give me peace. Up until that moment, I still carried a small bit of lingering guilt regarding what happened in 2002. Every once and a while, when passing the bronze memorial plaques of Dean Sutin, Professor Blackwell, and Angela Dales, located near ASL's front entrance, I sometimes wondered, "what if ?"

What if I reported Peter O's strange conduct to President Ellsworth?

What if I didn't ask for a sign that I would make it in law school before receiving my vision?

What if I just gave him a ride to Cleveland?

All of my remaining inner fault completely vanished after the heroic Zeb Blackwell bravely took the stand. Zeb sent Peter O into exile with the lasting words no one in that courtroom will ever forget:

"I hope, Peter, you can understand that I love you."

And with that, the young man chose to move on with his life, without hate flooding his soul. When he eventually moved back to Texas, Zeb didn't allow his tribulations to hold him back or define him. He let Grundy go. He successfully defied the wickedness and snares of the Devil.

So, too, did I.

## About the Author

Jeremy M. Burnside is a trial attorney in Portsmouth, Ohio. He represents the little guy against big insurance companies and is a dedicated advocate against tort "de-form." He has been recognized by his peers as an *Ohio Super Lawyer Rising Star*, a top-40 civil trial attorney under 40, and has been included in the National Trial Lawyers' *Top 100 Trial Lawyers* list. Jeremy handles many serious personal injury, nursing home neglect, brain injury, and wrongful death cases in Ohio and in Kentucky, where he is also licensed to practice.

The self-proclaimed "worst law student in Appalachian history" grew up on the near-West Side of Cleveland, but completed his undergraduate and graduate work at the University of Charleston (WV) and the Appalachian School of Law, respectively. After practicing law in Cleveland for five years, Jeremy returned to Appalachia where he opened up his current practice and met his wife.

Jeremy is married to a local real estate broker, Maddie Burnside. They have a daughter, Maura Rose, and expect a second child in August 2015. The Burnsides share office space in an old church that they repurposed, with the former worship area now serving Jeremy's clients as a mock-trial courtroom.

Jeremy enjoys rowing, hiking with his family, and heavy metal music. He can be contacted through his website, www.jburnsidelaw.com, or directly by email at jeremy@jburnsidelaw.com.

# Acknowledgments

First and foremost, I want to thank Zeb Blackwell for helping me edit this book. Choosing to do so in light of the content speaks more volumes of the young man's strength. That, and he is one hell-of-an-editor! Without him, I believe I may have shelved my story entirely.

I would like to express my appreciation to all others who read through some pretty terrible drafts of this book and provided comments. These folks are too numerous to name, but I can promise that every comment was, and is, deeply appreciated—especially the bad ones.

I would like to thank Judge Mark Painter and his wife, Sue Ann, for believing in me and for placing her publishing company's name on my story. Also to Tony Brunsman, Sue Ann's partner, and the staff at Cincinnati Book Publishing for their good work and support of this endeavor. Judge Painter personally did the copy editing, design, and formatting of the text.

I want to thank my classmates and professors at ASL, all of whom helped me overcome substantial odds and forced me to grow up. And as you all know (or should know), any and all parallels between the fictional characters and you all are merely coincidental—especially in the dialogue. As you can imagine, I only felt bitterness to substantiate that large chip on my shoulder—so I only wrote about what I felt, not what actually happened. In real life, you all expressed kindness and direction to help me become a good lawyer and a better person, and I am forever indebted to you.

To all the staff members of ASL during that time, most of whom were actually named herein, you also have a special place in my heart. I'm sure much of what was said between us in this book is inaccurate, but the message is clear: I could not have passed without your support. Thank you for believing in me, Admissions and Dean Lund!

I would be remiss not to publicly thank Tim and Liz Murphy for their part in this chapter of my life. Also to the staff and members of the 2001–2002 West Virginia Legislature for lighting my way.

Above all, I want to thank my wife, Maddie, and all of my close friends and family members who continue to support my crazy ideas and help me overachieve despite how annoying I may become.

Lastly, I want to thank my mom, who still encourages me to pray.

Jeremy Burnside
May 2015

# Photos

The face of fall-semester recklessness (November 2001)

01/10/2002

**Appalachian School of Law**

**Grade Report Form**

**Fall 2001**

**Burnside, Jeremy M.**

| Course | Course Description | Grade | Class Grade | Credits Attempted | Credits Received | Quality Points |
|---|---|---|---|---|---|---|
| LAW0100 | *Introduction to Law | P | | 2.00 | 2.00 | 0.00 |
| LAW0102 | Contracts I | D | | 3.00 | 3.00 | 3.00 |
| LAW0104 | Property I | C+ | | 3.00 | 3.00 | 6.99 |
| LAW0110 | Torts | D+ | | 4.00 | 4.00 | 5.32 |
| LAW0112 | Civil Procedure I | D+ | | 2.00 | 2.00 | 2.66 |
| LAW0198 | Legal Process I | B- | | 3.00 | 3.00 | 8.01 |
| | | | TOTALS | 17.00 | 17.00 | 25.98 |

**Semester GPA** 1.73

**Cumulative GPA** 1.73

Registrar

ASL 2001 transcript: The document that sparked my vision quest.

I took these two photos of the ASL campus on January 16, 2002, perhaps to remind myself of how gloomy the world was that day.

*Appalachian School of Law Family presents the Inaugural:*

# ASL Memorial 5k

*5K Run – 2 Mile Walk*

Proceeds benefit the families of:

*Tom Blackwell* *Anthony Sutin* *Angela Dales*

**WHEN:** **Saturday, April 13, 2002** -- 8:30 a.m. Start

**WHERE:** Appalachian School of Law- Grundy, V.a. (Rt. 460)

**Course:** **5k/Walk** - Downtown Grundy Area

**T-Shirts:** *FREE* for First 50 Entrants (X-Large Only)

**Awards:** **Trophies** will be awarded to top overall male/female run winners
**Medals** will be given to top two placers in each run category.
**Memorial Ribbons** will be given to top 5 male/female walkers

The 2002 ASL Memorial 5k race form.

View of the 2002 ASL Memorial 5k starting line

My saviors at the 2002 Memorial 5k registration table

Lisa and Zeb Blackwell after the finish
of the 2002 ASL Memorial 5k

www.vamountaineer.com

ay 9, 2002 — 2 Sections, Plus Supplements—50¢

# Flood Ravages Hurley Area

## Damages Expected to Exceed $50 Million; Clean-Up Begins

by Cathy St. Clair
*News Editor*

Two men died and countless numbers were left homeless Thursday after floodwaters ravaged the Hurley community, leaving in their path a minimum of $50 million-plus worth of damage, according to county officials.

Bural Blankenship, 85 and Robert

the bus and evacuate the students t a nearby home.

Access to the Hurley communit was restricted through Sunday t allow only residents, their families emergency workers and the media t enter the areas hardest hit by flood ing. Law enforcement officials stoo guard at key access points, includin those at Elkins Branch and acros Rockhouse Mountain until Monday

THE VIRGINIA MOUNTAINEER

Buchanan County's Family Newspaper — www.vamountaineer.com

Vol. 80, No. 18 — Grundy, Virginia 24614 • Thursday, May 2, 2002 — 2 Sections, Plus Supplements—50¢

# Blast Rocks Town of Grundy

## Four Injured; 45 Vehicles, 8 Buildings Damaged When Shot Goes Awry

by Cathy St. Clair
*News Editor*

Four people were injured and 45 vehicles and eight buildings were damaged last Wednesday when something went wrong with a blast at the Grundy Flood Control Project redevelopment site sending rock and debris raining down on a section of the downtown area.

The cause of the errant blast remains under investigation (see related story, this issue).

Rail service was suspended for a period of time Wednesday -- delay-

track damaged by the falling rock and debris was replaced.

Broken glass, rock and shards of metal littered parking areas and side streets and stunned employees, who were in the buildings most heavily impacted by the blast wandered around outside, along with others who drove into to town, to survey the damage for themselves.

Cars were parked in lots with shattered glass and dents, flat tires and in some cases, still had the rocks

windshields.

Some people could be heard describing the area as looking like a "war zone."

The incident occurred around 5 p.m. last Wednesday as a scheduled blast was carried out. However, instead of the routine, this time, rocks spewed out past the back street and over the roofs of buildings lining Main Street to land on the front street and as far as the Grundy Community Center roof.

area for a time after fly rock apparently struck transformers on the pole, cutting off service to the buildings hardest hit by the blast debris.

"We are just blessed that nobody's dead," said Town Manager Chuck Crabtree.

His comment was echoed time and again throughout the town even as the arduous task of clean-up was mounted.

Matthew Pham, a third year law student at the Appalachian School of

across from the blast site Wednesday evening.

He said when the blast went off, his windows rattled and he assumed it was a normal blast -- something most Grundy residents have become accustomed to in the past few months since work began on the massive flood control project.

However, this time, Pham said, something was different. He said the rattling seemed a little longer and a second sound, which he said followed

Cover pages from May 2, 2002 and May 9, 2002.
Courtesy of *The Virginia Mountaineer*

My hangout at Breaks Interstate Park,
where everything finally made sense to me.

I am sworn-in as an attorney to practice law in Ohio:
November 2004, Columbus, Ohio
From left: Helen Romanowski (maternal grandmother), My mom, Mary, me, "Hammer" Mike Burnside, and Ruth Burnside (paternal grandmother).

"Hammer" Mike Burnside
Cleveland City Steel Hauler - West Virginia Boy
Biker - Ass Kicker.

Maddie Burnside and me - Browns fans.